Revision notes

D0550696

Intermediate 2

Maths

revision notes

Text copyright © 2002 Ken Nisbet
Design and layout copyright © 2002 Leckie & Leckie Ltd
Cover image © Caleb Rutherford and Science Photo Library

1st edition (reprinted 2005, 2006 twice)

All rights reserved. No part of this publication may be reproduced, stored in a retrieval system, or transmitted in any form or by any means, electronic, mechanical, photocopying, recording or otherwise, without prior permission in writing from Leckie & Leckie Ltd. Legal action will be taken by Leckie & Leckie Ltd against any infringement of our copyright.

ISBN 1-898890-14-5
ISBN-13 978-1-898890-14-0

Published by
Leckie & Leckie Ltd, 3rd Floor, 4 Queen Street, Edinburgh EH2 1JE
Tel: 0131 220 6831 Fax: 0131 225 9987
enquiries@leckieandleckie.co.uk www.leckieandleckie.co.uk

Special thanks to
Julie Barclay (design), Merlyn Gudgeon (illustration) and Caleb Rutherford (cover design)

A CIP Catalogue record for this book is available from the British Library.

Leckie & Leckie is a division of Huveaux plc.

Ken Nisbet

Contents

Unit 1

Unit 2

Unit 3

Introduction

These Revision Notes are intended to prepare you for the SQA Intermediate 2 Mathematics Exam. They have been written to fit the Unit Structure of the Mathematics Intermediate 2 Course as laid down in the National Course Specification Document.

The structure is:

Mandatory:	Mathematics 1 (Int 2) Unit 1 of these Notes
	Mathematics 2 (Int 2) Unit 2 of these Notes
Optional:	Mathematics 3 (Int 2) Unit 3 of these Notes

Note that the alternative unit 'Applications of Mathematics (Int 2)' is not covered by these notes. It would be expected that any candidate taking the Mathematics Intermediate 2 Course and intending to continue studying Mathematics beyond Intermediate 2 will not sit the alternative 'Applications of Mathematics' Unit.

In these notes key points have been emphasised, vital facts have been clearly summarised and all necessary techniques illustrated with a host of worked examples. Calculator hints are indicated by ▭. At all times the language used and the style of explanation are such that you can easily relate to the ideas and thus gain necessary understanding. A comprehensive index has been provided for quick access to particular topics, terms and ideas.

Decimal Places

Decimal places are counted immediately to the right of the decimal point.

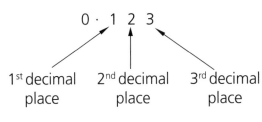

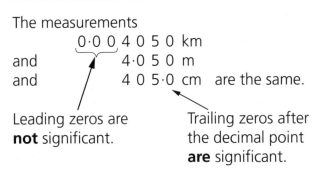

0 · 1 2 3

1st decimal place — 2nd decimal place — 3rd decimal place

Significant Figures

The measurements

0·0 0 4 0 5 0 km
and 4·0 5 0 m
and 4 0 5·0 cm are the same.

Leading zeros are **not** significant.

Trailing zeros after the decimal point **are** significant.

Significant figures are counted immediately to the right of any leading zeros:

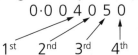

0·0 0 4 0 5 0

1st 2nd 3rd 4th significant figure

Rounding Measurements

The Rounding Rules ···7 8 3 4 7 2···

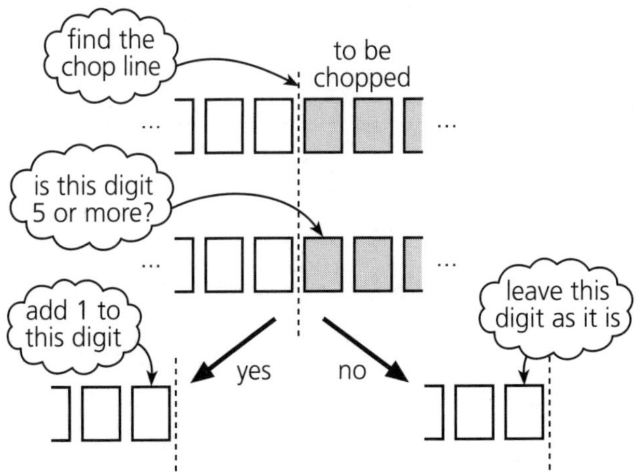

Example 1.1

To how many decimal places are these measurements written?

(a) 8·2 m (b) 0·03 kg (c) 14·803 s

Solution

(a) 1 decimal place (d. p.)
(b) 2 d. p.
(c) 3 d. p.

Example 1.2

How many significant figures do the following measurements have?

(a) 26·5 cm (b) 20·04 kg
(c) 0·020 m^2 (d) 260 tonnes

Solution

(a) 3 significant figures (s. f.)
(b) 4 s. f.
(c) 2 s. f.
(d) 2 s. f. (if it is to the nearest 10 tonnes)
or
3 s. f. (if it is to the nearest 1 tonne)

Example 1.3

Round each of these measurements to
(i) 3 significant figures (ii) 1 significant figure.

(a) 24·66 cm (b) 0·2495 g

Solution

(a) (i) 24·66 ≑ 24·7 cm (to 3 s. f.)
(ii) 24·66 ≑ 20 cm (to 1 s. f.)
(b) (i) 0·2495 ≑ 0·250 g (to 3 s. f.)
(ii) 0·2495 ≑ 0·2 g (to 1 s. f.)

1. Percentages and Significant Figures

Advice on Rounding

It is useful to draw number lines:

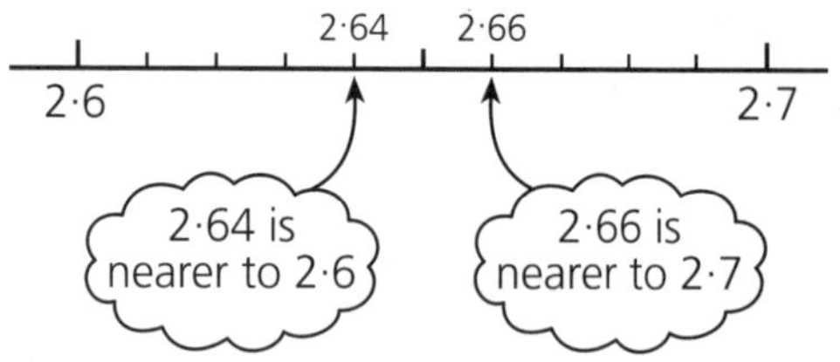

Never round the values in a calculation until the final answer is obtained. Calculating with rounded numbers leads to inaccurate results.

Do not leave more significant figures in the answer to a calculation than there were in the measurements you used for the calculation. (Final accuracy depends on initial accuracy!)

Basic Percentage Calculations

Type 1 Finding a % of a quantity

step 1 Divide the percentage number by 100.

step 2 Multiply by the quantity.

Type 2 Expressing one quantity as a % of another quantity

step 1 Divide the 1st quantity by the 2nd quantity.

step 2 Multiply by 100% (to change the fraction to a percentage).

Example 1.4

VAT (Value Added Tax) is charged at 17·5%. Find, to the nearest penny, the VAT added to a bill of £525.

Solution

17·5% of £525 = $\frac{17\cdot5}{100} \times 525$

(divide by 100, multiply by 525)

= 91·875

The VAT is **£91·88** (to nearest penny).

Example 1.5

A CD is sold at £14 for a profit of £4. Express this profit as a % of the buying price (i.e. the price the shop paid for the CD).

Solution

Profit £4 with a buying price of £10.

% Profit = $\frac{4}{10} \times 100\%$

= **40%**

Using a Multiplier

Appreciation is when a value increases.

To increase £230, for example, by 15%:

115% = $\frac{115}{100}$ = 1·15 (the multiplier)

The answer is given by:
£230 × 1·15 = £264·50

Check this on your calculator.

Depreciation is when a value decreases.

To decrease £230, for example, by 15%:

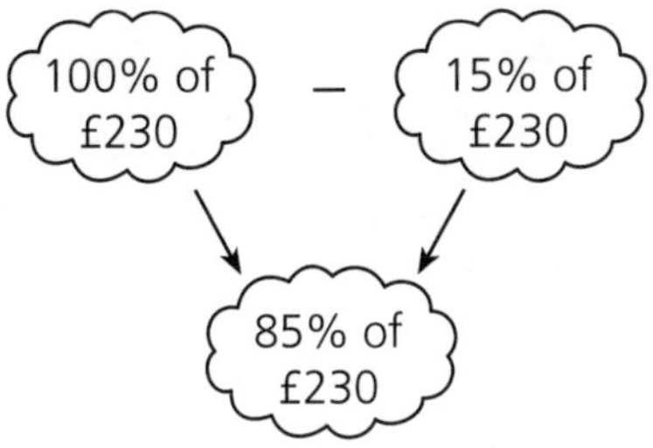

85% = $\frac{85}{100}$ = 0·85 (the multiplier)
The answer is given by:
£230 × 0·85 = £195·50

Example 1.6

A house bought for £90 000 appreciates in value by 5% each year. What is it worth after 3 years? (Give your answer to the nearest £1000.)

Solution
100% + 5% = 105% = $\frac{105}{100}$ = 1·05
(This is the multiplier.)

Value at start = £90 000
After 1 year: £90 000 × 1·05 = £94 500
After 2 years: £94 500 × 1·05 = £99 225
After 3 years: £99 225 × 1·05 = £104 186·25

Final value = **£104 000** (to the nearest £1000)

Example 1.7

Company shares worth £1 200 depreciate in value over a month by 12% but then appreciate by 13% over the next month. Are they now worth more or less than before?

Solution
After 1st month: £1200 × 0·88 = £1056
(100% – 12% = 88% = 0·88 is the multiplier.)

After 2nd month: £1056 × 1·13 = £1193·28
(100% + 13% = 113% = 1·13 is the multiplier.)

So they are worth **£6·72 less**.

1. Percentages and Significant Figures

Compound Interest

Money which is invested (called the **principal**) usually grows in value. This extra value is called **interest**.

Interest is calculated as a percentage of the principal invested. The percentage used for this calculation is called the **rate of interest**.

The letters p.a. stand for 'per annum' and mean that the interest is calculated for 1 complete year.

Principal + Interest = Amount

When the interest is not withdrawn but is added to the investment, it will also start to gain interest. This is called **compound interest**.

Example 1.8

Calculate the compound interest and the final amount for an investment of £950 for 2 years at 6% p.a.

Solution

$100\% + 6\% = 106\% = \frac{106}{100} = 1{\cdot}06$

(This is the multiplier.)

1st year: Amount = £950 × 1·06 = £1007
2nd year: Amount = £1007 × 1·06 = £1067·42
i.e. Final Amount = £1067·42
Compound interest = £1067·42 – £950
= **£117·42**

Further Percentage Calculations

Type 3 Given the final amount after a % increase or decrease, finding the original amount before the change

step 1 For an increase add the % to 100. For a decrease subtract the % from 100.

step 2 Divide the final amount by the answer to step 1. (This calculates 1% of the amount.)

step 3 Multiply by 100. (This calculates 100% of the original amount.)

Example 1.9

After a 15% sales reduction, a TV costs £306. What was its original price?

Solution

100% – 15% = 85% ⟷ £306
So 1% ⟷ $£\frac{306}{85}$
So 100% ⟷ $£\frac{306}{85} \times 100$
= £360

Original price was **£360**.

Inflation

Over time, prices tend to increase. The **inflation rate** measures this increase. For example, during 2000 in the UK, the annual inflation rate was 3%.

Example 1.10

By how much should a weekly pay packet of £230 increase to keep in line with an inflation rate of 4·2% over a year?

Solution

$4{\cdot}2\%$ of £230 = $\frac{4{\cdot}2}{100} \times 230$ = £9·66

A **£9·66** increase would be needed.

Reminders

Area is measured in square units. A square centimetre is shown on the right.

1 cm^2: 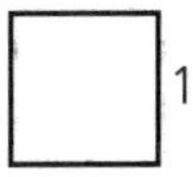

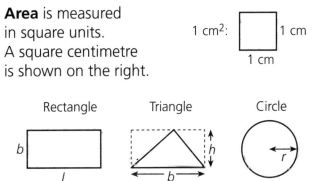

Rectangle | Triangle | Circle

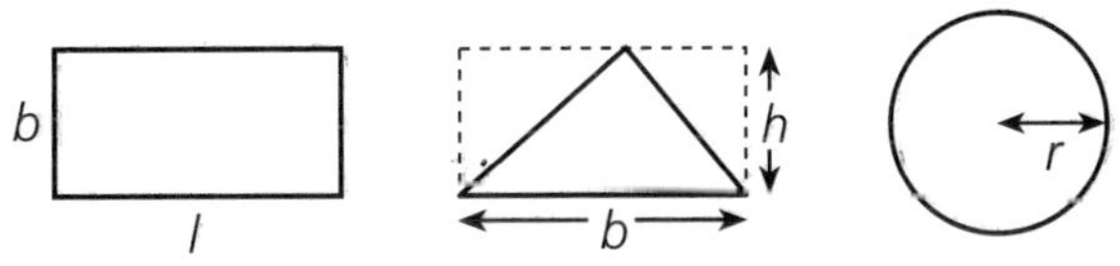

$A = l \times b$ | $A = \frac{1}{2}b \times h$ | $A = \pi r^2$

Volume is measured in cube units. A centimetre cube is shown on the right.

1 cm^3: 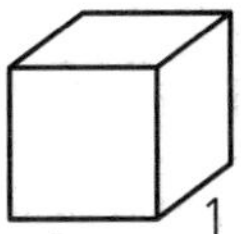

It has different names:

1 cubic centimetre (1 cc)

or 1 millilitre (1 ml)

so 1000 cm^3 = 1 litre.

Spheres

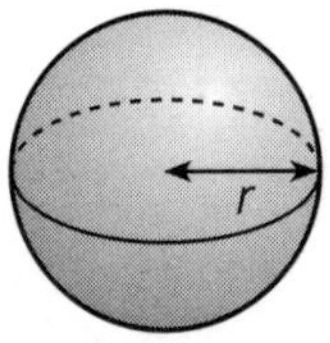

The volume, V unit^3, of a sphere with radius r units is given by:

$$V = \frac{4}{3}\pi r^3$$

Use the following key sequence:

[4] [÷] [3] [×] [π] [×] ...(enter radius)... [y^x] [3] [=]

(or [x^y] or [^] in place of [y^x])

Half a sphere is called a **hemisphere**.

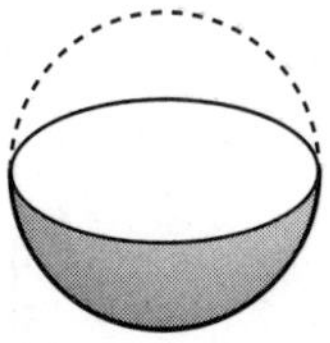

To find its volume, calculate the volume of the whole sphere then divide by 2.

(Remember that if you are given the diameter then divide it by 2 to get the radius, before using the volume formula).

Example 2.1

Find the area of a circle with diameter 13 cm.

Solution

Use $A = \pi r^2$ with $r = 6{\cdot}5$ cm (half the diameter)

So $A = \pi \times 6{\cdot}5^2$

$= 132{\cdot}73 \ldots$

$\doteqdot 132{\cdot}7$ cm^2 (to 1 d. p.)

Example 2.2

Find the volume of a sphere with diameter 14 cm. (Give your answer to 3 significant figures.)

Solution

Use $V = \frac{4}{3}\pi r^3$ with $r = 7$ cm (half the diameter)

So $V = \frac{4}{3} \times \pi \times 7^3$

$= 1436{\cdot}75 \ldots$

$\doteqdot 1440$ cm^3 (to 3 s. f.)

2. Volumes of Solids

Cones

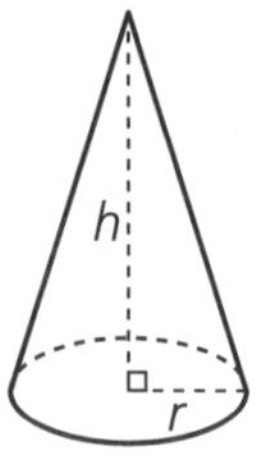

The volume, V unit^3, of a cone with perpendicular height h units and radius of base r units is given by

$$V = \tfrac{1}{3}\pi r^2 h$$

Use the following key sequence:

[1] [÷] [3] [×] [π] [×] ...(enter radius)... [x^2] [×] ...(enter height)... [=]

Prisms

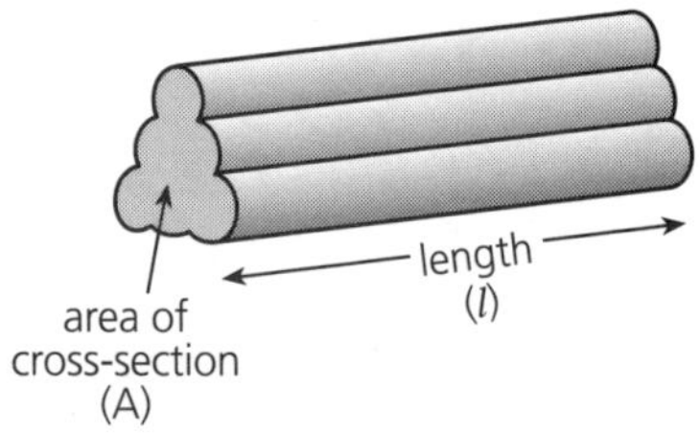

The volume, V unit^3, of a prism with area of cross-section A unit^2 and length l units is given by

$$V = A \times l$$

Special Prisms

Cylinder:

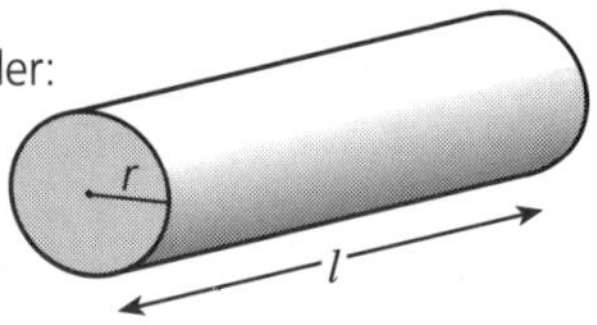

$V = \pi r^2 \times l$

Area of cross-section is the area of a circle.

Triangular prism:

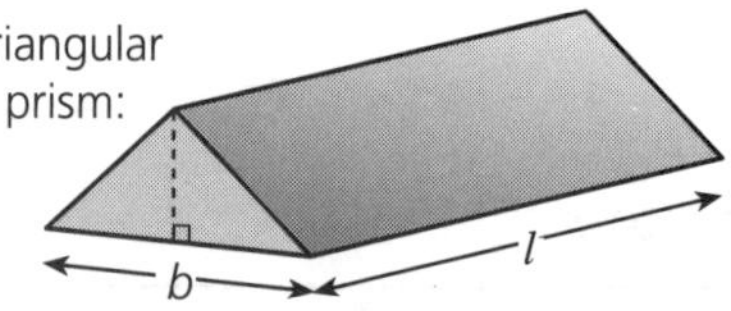

$V = \tfrac{1}{2}bh \times l$

Area of cross-section is the area of a triangle.

Cuboid:

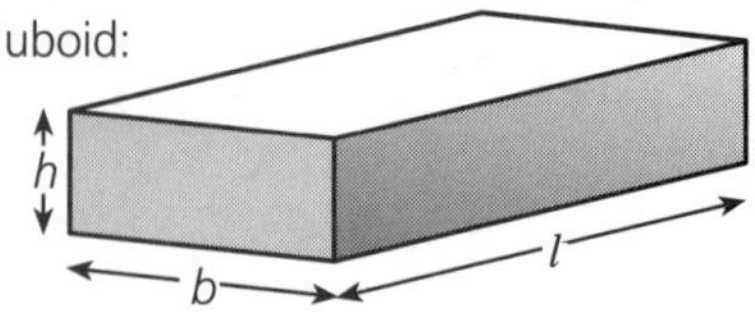

$V = bh \times l$

Area of cross-section is the area of a rectangle.

Example 2.3

An ice cream cone is 12 cm long with diameter 7 cm at the top. How many 1-litre tubs of ice cream are required to fill 150 of these cones?

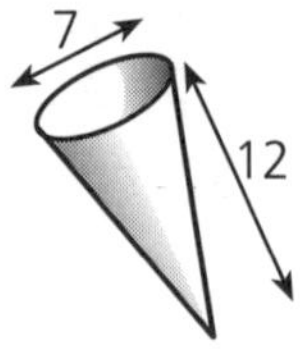

Solution

Use $V = \tfrac{1}{3}\pi r^2 h$ with $r = 3{\cdot}5$ cm (half the diameter)

and $h = 12$ cm

so $V = \tfrac{1}{3} \times \pi \times 3{\cdot}5^2 \times 12$

$= 153{\cdot}938\ldots$

With 150 cones having volume

$= 153{\cdot}938\ldots \times 150$

$= 23\ 090{\cdot}7\ldots$ cm^3

$= 23{\cdot}09\ldots$ litres (1000 cm^3 = 1 litre)

So **24** 1-litre tubs would be required. (Notice that 23 tubs would not supply quite enough ice cream.)

Example 2.4

Calculate the volume of this prism-shaped bread bin. The cross-section consists of a 12·5 cm × 18 cm rectangle and a quarter circle with radius 18 cm.

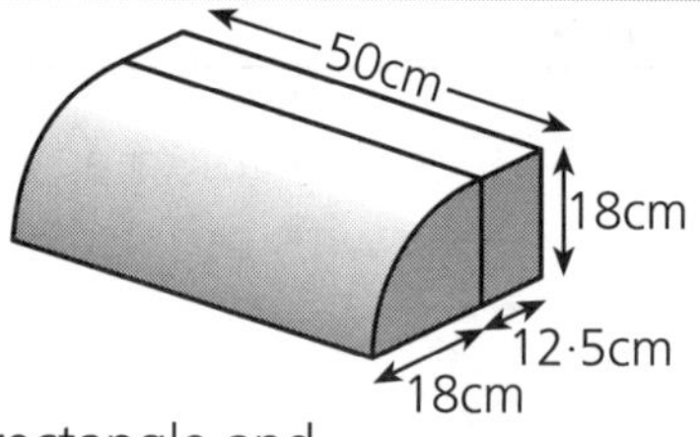

Solution

Area of cross-section $= \tfrac{1}{4}$circle + rectangle

$= \tfrac{1}{4} \times \pi \times 18^2 + 12{\cdot}5 \times 18$

$= 254{\cdot}46\ldots + 225$

$= 479{\cdot}46\ldots$

Volume = area of cross-section × length

$= 479{\cdot}46\ldots \times 50$

$= 23\ 973{\cdot}4\ldots$ cm^3

$\doteq$ **24 000 cm³** (to 3 s. f.)

What is Gradient?

Gradient is a number that measures the slope of a line. Divide the vertical distance by the horizontal distance:

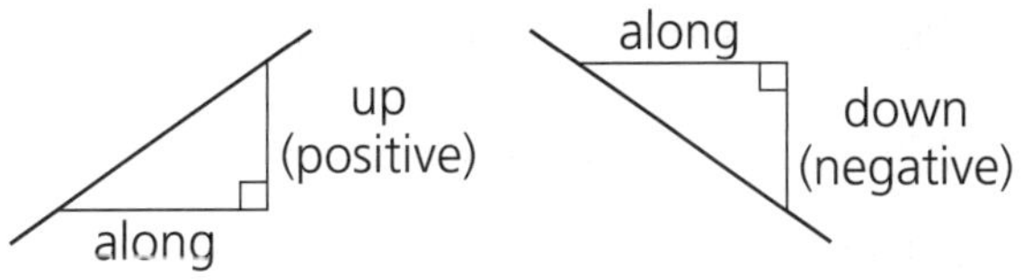

$$\text{Gradient} = \frac{\text{distance up or down}}{\text{distance along}}$$

Gradient Diagram

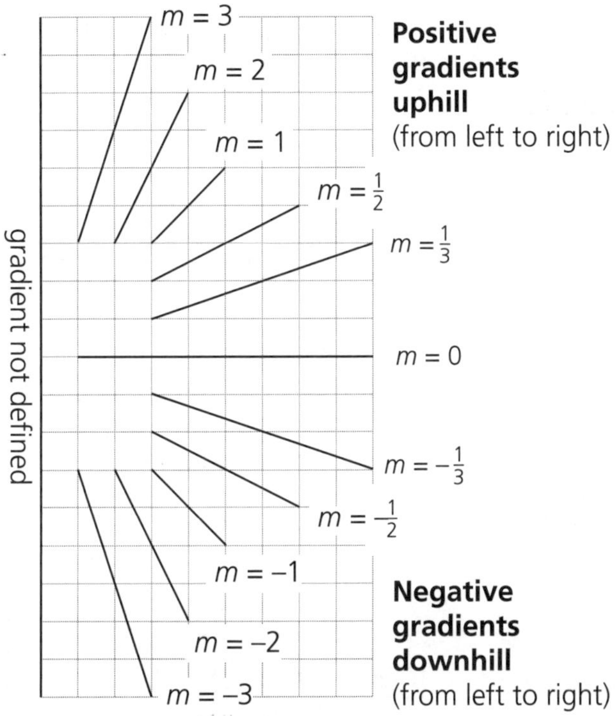

Gradient Formula for Points

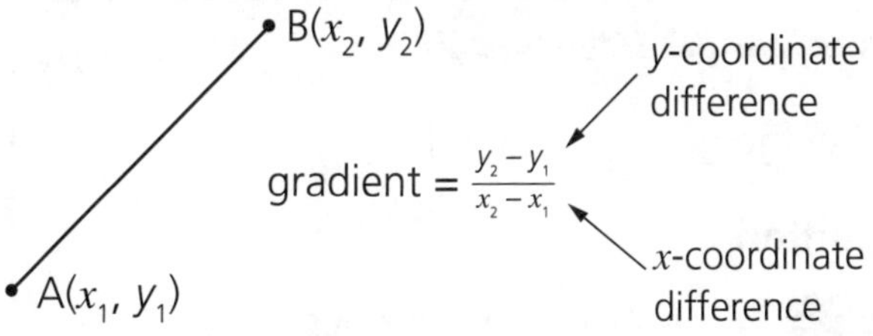

Note: $\frac{y_1 - y_2}{x_1 - x_2}$ gives the same result. So you can swap **both** top or bottom but not just one.

Example 3.1

Give the gradient of each line:

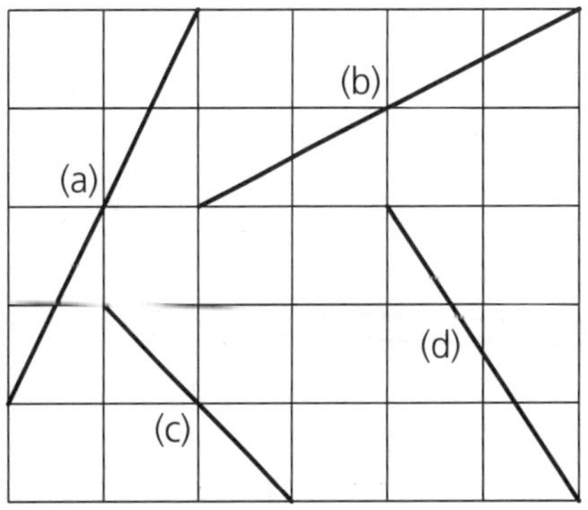

Solution

(a) 2 up, 1 along so gradient = $\frac{2}{1}$ = **2**

(b) 1 up, 2 along so gradient = $\mathbf{\frac{1}{2}}$

(c) 1 down, 1 along so gradient = $\frac{-1}{1}$ = **−1**

(d) 3 down, 2 along so gradient = $\frac{-3}{2}$ = $\mathbf{-\frac{3}{2}}$

Example 3.2

Calculate the gradient of the line joining (−1, 3) and (2, −3).

Solution

$$\begin{aligned}\text{gradient} &= \frac{3-(-3)}{-1-2}\\ &= \frac{3+3}{-1-2}\\ &= \frac{6}{-3}\\ &= \mathbf{-2}\end{aligned}$$

Graphs from Equations

To draw the graph of a line from its equation there are two methods:

Method 1: Plot some points

step 1 Choose a few values for x and use the equation to calculate the corresponding values of y. It is helpful to put all the values in a table.

step 2 Draw a coordinate diagram. Since each pair of values in your table will be used as coordinates of a point, you can decide on a suitable scale for the two axes by looking at the table.

step 3 Plot the points on your diagram and draw a line through them.

Example 3.3 (Method 1)

Draw the graph $y = 2x + 1$

Solution

step 1 A table of values is:

x	-2	-1	0	1	2
y	-3	-1	1	3	5

(This gives points $(-2, -3)$, $(-1, -1)$, $(0, 1)$, $(1, 3)$ and $(2, 5)$.)

step 2

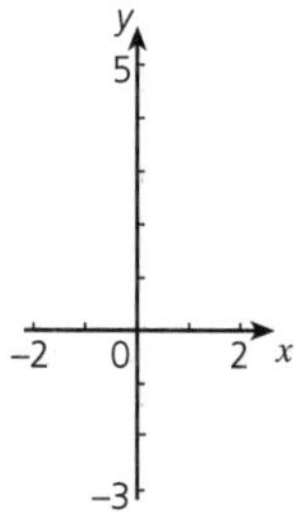

(The scales -2 to 2 on the x-axis and -3 to 5 on the y-axis can be seen from the table of values above.)

step 3

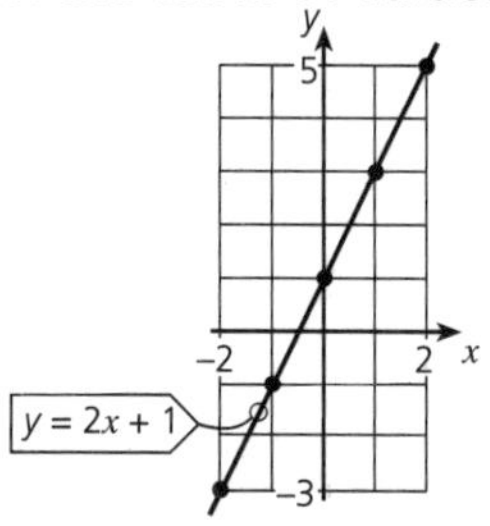

Method 2: Use gradient and *y*-intercept

step 1 If necessary, rearrange the equation into the form: $y = ax + b$

step 2 Identify the gradient, a, and the y-intercept, $(0, b)$, where the line crosses the y-axis.

step 3 Use the information to sketch the graph. (The gradient diagram on page 9 may help.)

Example 3.3 (Method 2)

Draw the graph $y - 2x = 1$

Solution

step 1 Add $2x$ to both sides to get:

$$y = 2x + 1$$

step 2 The gradient is 2. The y-intercept is $(0, 1)$.

step 3

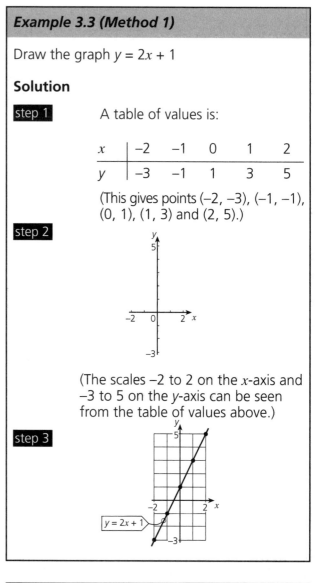

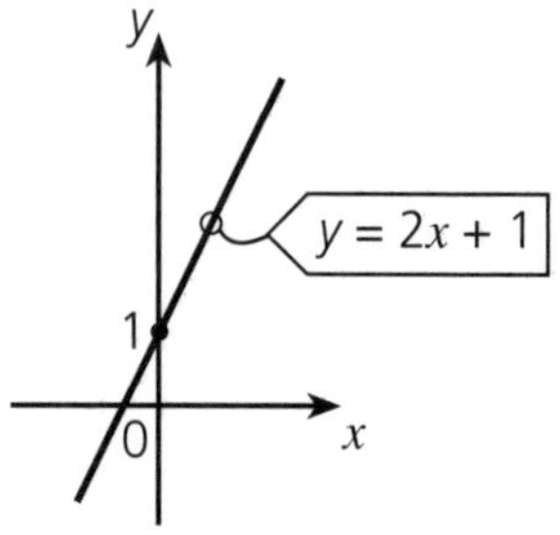

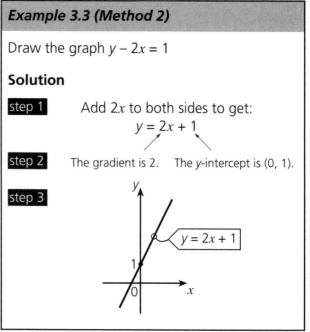

Equations from Graphs

To find the equation of a line from its graph:

step 1 Calculate the gradient of the line. To do this you will need to draw a triangle on the grid with the sloping side along the line. Now use:

$$\text{Gradient} = \frac{\text{distance up or down}}{\text{distance along}}$$

step 2 Find the y-intercept: note the number on the y-axis where the line crosses.

step 3 The equation is:

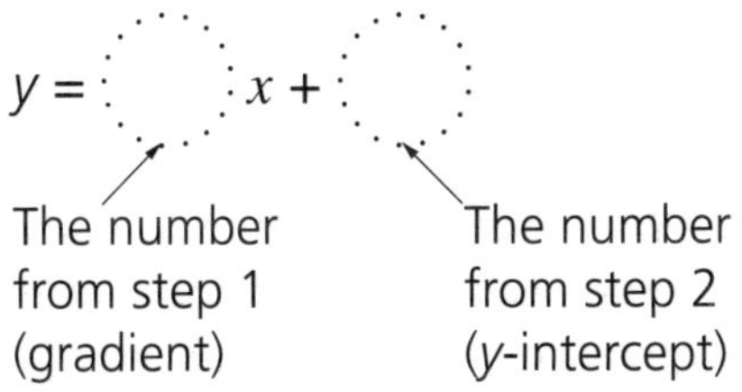

Example 3.4

Find the equation of these lines:

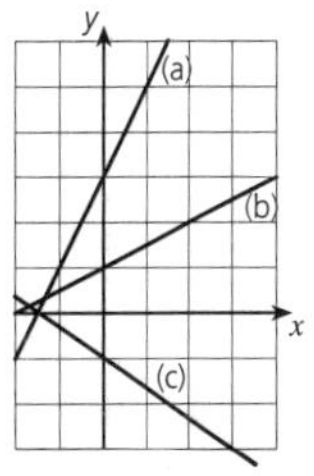

Solution

(a)

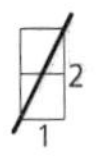

gradient $= \frac{2}{1} = 2$
y-intercept gives 3
equation: $y = 2x + 3$

(b)

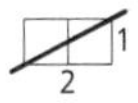

gradient $= \frac{1}{2}$
y-intercept gives 1
equation: $y = \frac{1}{2}x + 1$

(c)

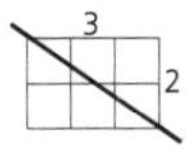

gradient $= \frac{-2}{3} = -\frac{2}{3}$
y-intercept gives -1
equation: $y = -\frac{2}{3}x - 1$

Special Lines

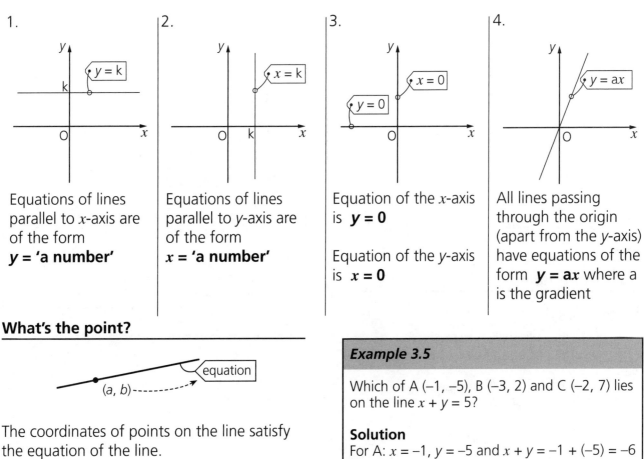

1.

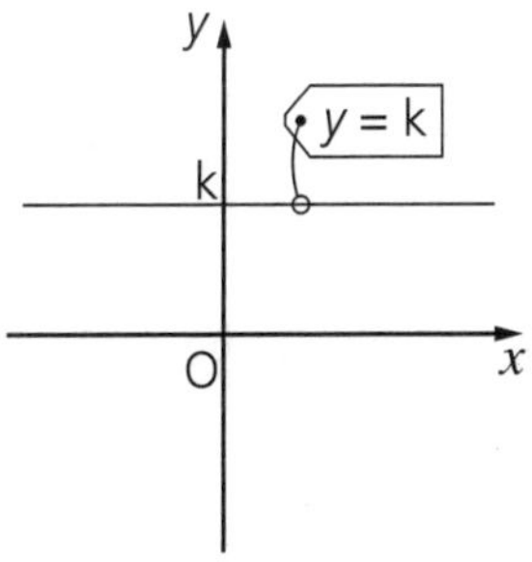

Equations of lines parallel to x-axis are of the form
y = 'a number'

2.

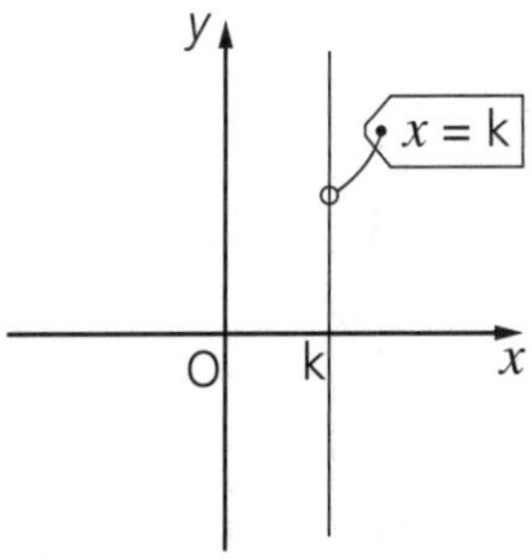

Equations of lines parallel to y-axis are of the form
x = 'a number'

3.

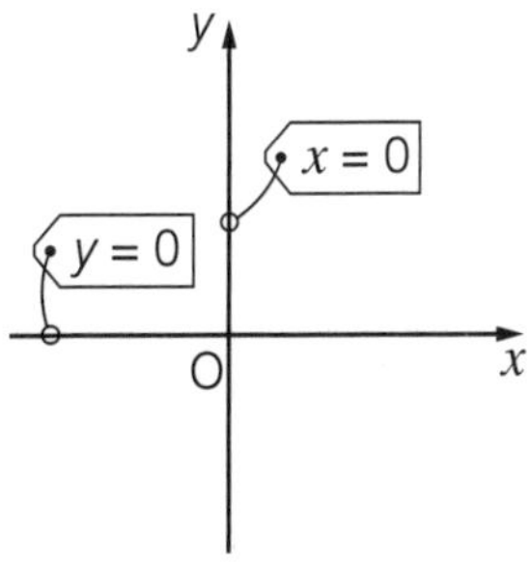

Equation of the x-axis is $\boldsymbol{y = 0}$

Equation of the y-axis is $\boldsymbol{x = 0}$

4.

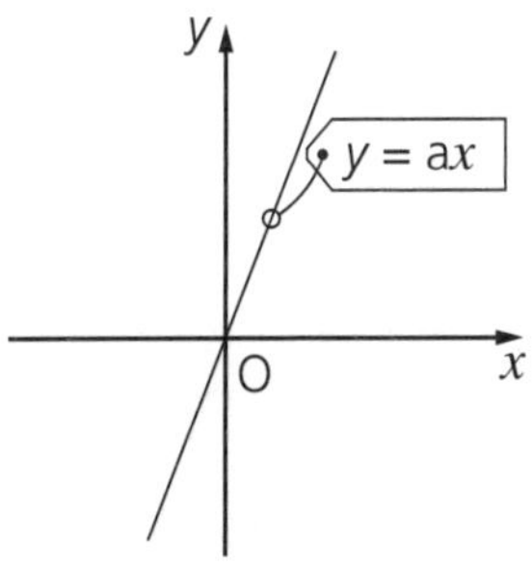

All lines passing through the origin (apart from the y-axis) have equations of the form $\boldsymbol{y = ax}$ where a is the gradient

What's the point?

The coordinates of points on the line satisfy the equation of the line.

The coordinates of points not on the line don't satisfy the equation of the line.

Example 3.5

Which of A (–1, –5), B (–3, 2) and C (–2, 7) lies on the line $x + y = 5$?

Solution

For A: $x = -1$, $y = -5$ and $x + y = -1 + (-5) = -6$
For B: $x = -3$, $y = 2$ and $x + y = -3 + 2 = -1$
For C: $x = -2$, $y = 7$ and $x + y = -2 + 7 = 5$

Only **C** has coordinates that satisfy the equation so it lies on the line.

3. Linear Relationships

Parallel Lines

Lines which have the same gradient are parallel:

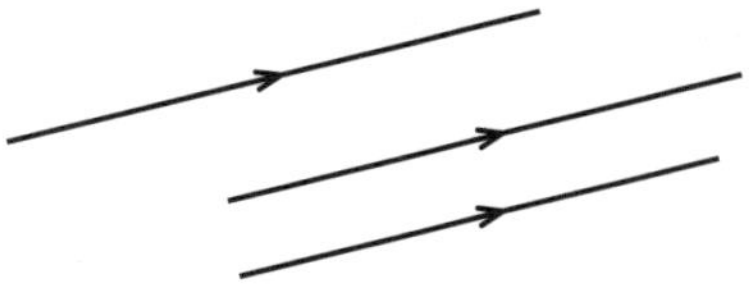

Other forms of equation for a line

$y + 4 = 3x$

$y = 1$

$2x = 3$

$2x - 3y = 2$

$x + 3y - 1 = 0$

$4 - 5x = y$

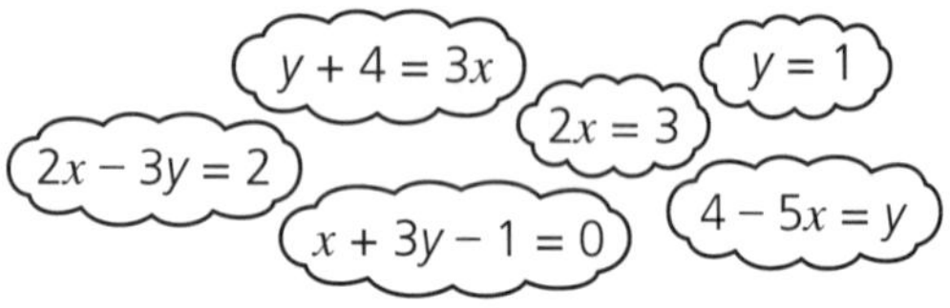

All these equations have an 'x-term' or a 'y-term' or both. The only other terms are numbers. These equations are all equations of straight lines.

> ### *Example 3.6*
>
> Are the lines $2y - 4x = 1$ and $y + 4 = 2x$ parallel?
>
> **Solution**
> $2y - 4x = 1$ (add $4x$ to both sides)
> $2y = 4x + 1$ (divide both sides by 2)
> $y = 2x + \frac{1}{2}$
>
> gradient is 2
>
> $y + 4 = 2x$ (subtract 4 from both sides)
> $y = 2x - 4$
>
> gradient is 2
>
> The lines have the same gradient and are therefore **parallel**.

4. Algebraic Operations

Adding and Subtracting Terms

Use the number line:

$-1 - 3 = -4$
$-1 + (-3) = -4$

$-1 + 3 = 2$
$-1 - (-3) = 2$

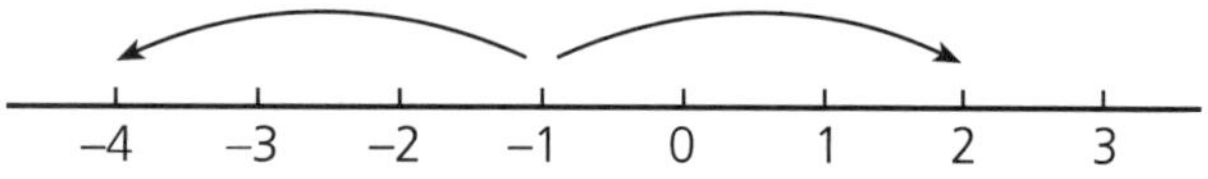

In the same way:

$-x - 3x = -4x$
$-x + (-3x) = -4x$

$-x + 3x = 2x$
$-x - (-3x) = 2x$

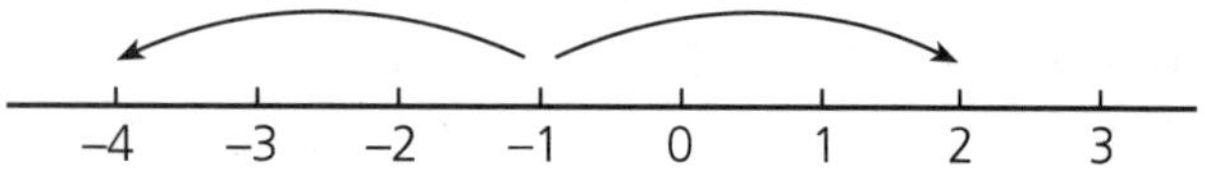

Multiplying Terms

Use the rules:

$\left. \begin{array}{l} \text{positive} \times \text{positive} \\ \text{negative} \times \text{negative} \end{array} \right\}$ positive

$\left. \begin{array}{l} \text{negative} \times \text{positive} \\ \text{positive} \times \text{negative} \end{array} \right\}$ negative

So $\underset{\text{(pos)}}{x} \times \underset{\text{(neg)}}{(-3x)} = \underset{\text{(neg)}}{-3x^2}$ and $\underset{\text{(neg)}}{-2a} \times \underset{\text{(neg)}}{(-3b)} = \underset{\text{(pos)}}{6ab}$

> ### *Example 4.1*
>
> Simplify: (a) $y - (-3y)$
> (b) $2x^2 + x - 5x^2$
> (c) $-3a \times 4a$
> (d) $-2x - 3x$
>
> **Solution**
> (a) $y - (-3y) = y + 3y = 4y$
> (Subtracting a negative is the same as adding.)
>
> (b) $2x^2 + x - 5x^2 = -3x^2 + x$
> ($2x^2$ and x cannot be added together but '2 lots of x^2' minus '5 lots of x^2' gives 'minus 3 lots of x^2')
>
> (c) $\underset{\text{(neg)}}{-3a} \times \underset{\text{(pos)}}{4a} = \underset{\text{(neg)}}{-12a^2}$
>
> (d) $-2x - 3x = -5x$
>
> compare: $-2 - 3 = -5$

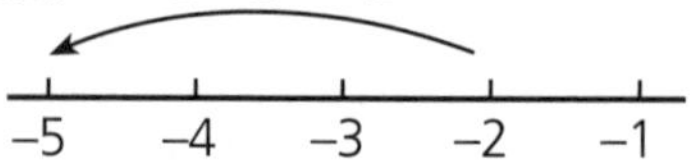

Ways of thinking and writing

	:	
	$3x$	'3 lots of x'
	$2x$	'2 lots of x'
for $1x$ write	x	'1 lot of x'
for $0x$ write	0	'no lots of x'
for $-1x$ write	$-x$	'minus 1 lot of x'
	$-2x$	'minus 2 lots of x'
	:	

x^3 'x cubed' means $x \times x \times x$

x^2 'x squared' means $x \times x$

$2x^2$ '2 lots of x^2'

$3(x + 1)$ '3 lots of $x + 1$'

Removing One Pair of Brackets

$3(x - 2)$ **means** '3 lots of $x - 2$'

$x - 2$
$x - 2$
$x - 2$

$3x - 6$ **written** — 3 lots of x gives $3x$; 3 lots of -2 gives -6

So $3(x - 2) = 3x - 6$

In general: $a(b + c) = ab + ac$

and $a(b + c + d) = ab + ac + ad$

Example 4.2

Write without brackets:

(a) $3(x + 2)$
(b) $-2(4 - y)$
(c) $-(x - x^2)$

Solution

(a) $3(x + 2) = \mathbf{3x + 6}$

(b) $-2(4 - y) = \mathbf{-8 + 2y}$

(c) $-(x - x^2)$ think of $-1(x - x^2)$
$= \mathbf{-x + x^2}$

Removing Two Pairs of Brackets

	2	3
1	1×2	1×3
4	4×2	4×3

This square has area:
5×5
$= (1 + 4)(2 + 3)$
or adding individual rectangles:
$1 \times 2 + 1 \times 3 + 4 \times 2 + 4 \times 3$

First numbers in each bracket; **O**utside two numbers; **I**nside two numbers; **L**ast numbers in each bracket

The rule is **F O I L**
which means: **F**irsts, **O**utsides, **I**nsides, **L**asts

Here is the pattern in general:

$(a + b)(c + d)$

Firsts: $(a + b)(c + d)$ ac
Outsides: $(a + b)(c + d)$ ad
Insides: $(a + b)(c + d)$ bc
Lasts: $(a + b)(c + d)$ bd

giving: $ac + ad + bc + bd$

Example 4.3

Multiply out $(3x - 2)(x - 4)$

Solution

Think like this:

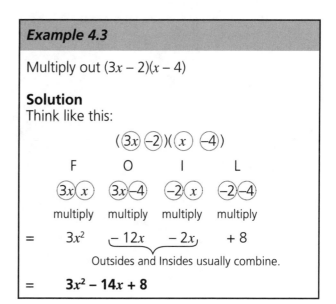

$(3x\ -2)(x\ -4)$

F	O	I	L
$3x$ x	$3x$ -4	-2 x	-2 -4
multiply	multiply	multiply	multiply

$= 3x^2 \quad - 12x \quad - 2x \quad + 8$

Outsides and Insides usually combine.

$= \mathbf{3x^2 - 14x + 8}$

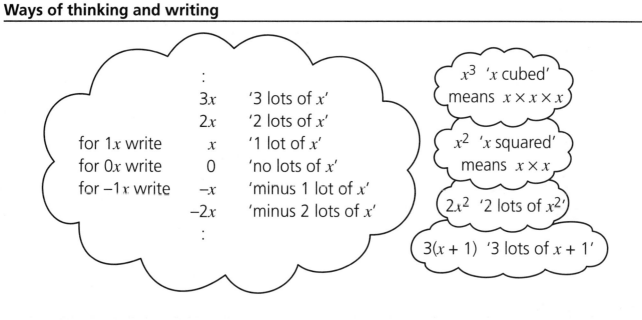

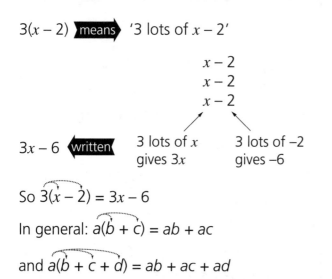

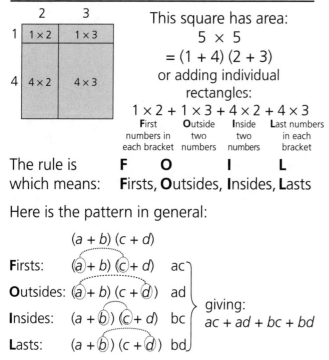

4. Algebraic Operations

Brackets Squared

Remember that a^2 means $a \times a$. So for examples like:

$$(2x - 1)^2 \qquad (a - b)^2 \qquad (2 + y)^2$$

you should write out a pair of equal brackets:

$(2x - 1)^2$ becomes $(2x - 1)(2x - 1)$
$(a - b)^2$ becomes $(a - b)(a - b)$
and $(2 + y)^2$ becomes $(2 + y)(2 + y)$

Larger Brackets

For expressions like:

$$(a + b)(c + d + e)$$

FOIL does not work.

Here is the pattern to use:

$(a + b)(c + d + e)$ giving $ac + ad + ae$

then $(a + b)(c + d + e)$ giving $bc + bd + be$

There is a total of six multiplications:

$(a + b)(c + d + e) = ac + ad + ae + bc + bd + be$

Example 4.4

Multiply out the brackets and collect like terms:
$(2x - 5)^2 - x(x + 2)$

Solution

$(2x - 5)(2x - 5) - x(x + 2)$

$= \underbrace{4x^2 - 10x - 10x + 25}_{\text{Using FOIL}} \underbrace{- x^2 - 2x}_{\text{one pair of brackets}}$

$= \mathbf{3x^2 - 22x + 25}$

($3x^2$ from $4x^2 - x^2$; $-22x$ from $-10x - 10x - 2x$)

Example 4.5

Write without brackets:
$(2x - 3)(x^2 + 2x - 5)$

Solution

First multiply by $2x$

$(2x - 3)(x^2 + 2x - 5)$ giving $2x^3 + 4x^2 - 10x$

Now multiply by -3

$(2x - 3)(x^2 + 2x - 5)$ giving $-3x^2 - 6x + 15$

So $(2x - 3)(x^2 + 2x - 5)$

$= 2x^3 + 4x^2 - 10x$ (from $2x$)

$-3x^2 - 6x + 15$ (from -3)

$= \mathbf{2x^3 + x^2 - 16x + 15}$

Common Factors

$30 = 1 \times 30$ or 2×15 or 3×10 or 6×5
so the factors of 30 are 1, 2, 3, 5, 6, 10, 15 and 30.

Similarly
$6a = 1 \times 6a$ or $2 \times 3a$ or $3 \times 2a$ or $6 \times a$
so the factors of $6a$ are 1, 2, 3, 6, a, $2a$, $3a$ and $6a$.

Consider $30ab + 6a$

$30ab$: factor $6a$ ($6a \times 5b$)

$6a$: factor $6a$ ($6a \times 1$)

So $30ab + 6a = 6a(5b + 1)$

The common factor $6a$ has been taken outside the brackets.

Here is another example:

$$6x^2 - 4x = 2x(3x - 2)$$

$6x^2$: factor $2x$ ($2x \times 3x$)

$4x$: factor $2x$ ($2x \times 2$)

The common factor $2x$ has been taken outside the brackets.

Difference of Two Squares

The square numbers:

Pick any two and find the difference (subtract them), e.g.

$100 - 49 = 51$	$64 - 36 = 28$
$10^2 - 7^2 = 3 \times 17$	or $8^2 - 6^2 = 2 \times 14$
$10^2 - 7^2 = (10 - 7)(10 + 7)$	$8^2 - 6^2 = (8 - 6)(8 + 6)$

In general the pattern is:

$$a^2 - b^2 = (a - b)(a + b)$$

Example 4.6

Factorise:

(a) $8x - 6$
(b) $7x^2 - 21x$
(c) $12xy^2 + 9x^2y$

Solution

(a) $8x - 6 = \mathbf{2(4x - 3)}$
$(2 \times 4x)$ (2×3) common factor 2

(b) $7x^2 - 21x = \mathbf{7x(x - 3)}$
$(7x \times x)$ $(7x \times 3)$ common factor $7x$

(c) $12xy^2 + 9x^2y = \mathbf{3xy(4y + 3x)}$
$(3xy \times 4y)$ $(3xy \times 3x)$ common factor $3xy$

Example 4.7

Factorise:

(a) $k^2 - m^2$
(b) $9x^2 - 1$
(c) $16y^2 - 25z^2$

Solution

(a) $k^2 - m^2 = \mathbf{(k - m)(k + m)}$

(b) $9x^2 - 1$ This is $(3x)^2 - 1^2$
$= \mathbf{(3x - 1)(3x + 1)}$

(c) $16y^2 - 25z^2$ This is $(4y)^2 - (5z)^2$
$= \mathbf{(4y - 5z)(4y + 5z)}$

4. Algebraic Operations

Quadratic Expressions

Multiplying out $(x + 2)(x + 3)$
gives $x^2 + 3x + 2x + 6$
(remember: F O I L)
and simplifies to $x^2 + 5x + 6$

Factorising $x^2 + 5x + 6$ reverses this process to get: $(x + 2)(x + 3)$

Here's another example:
Factorise $x^2 - x - 6$

step 1 Choose suitable Firsts and Lasts:

x^2...... 6

Firsts: $(x\quad)(x\quad)$ $x \times x = x^2$

Lasts: $(\quad 2)(\quad 3)$ $2 \times 3 = 6$

step 2 Write down the Outsides and Insides:

$(x\quad 2)(x\quad 3)$ Outsides: $3x$

$(x\quad 2)(x\quad 3)$ Insides: $2x$

step 3 Add or subtract to make the middle term:

$x^2 \; (-x) \; - 6$

↓

$2x - 3x$

Insides positive, Outsides negative

* If this step fails, redo **step 1** with different Firsts or Lasts (or swap the order of the Lasts if it makes a difference!) and repeat.

step 4 Put in the signs and check:

$x^2 - x - 6$

$= (x + 2)(x - 3)$ Multiply out using FOIL to check.

(positive, negative)

* If the check fails, redo **step 1** with different Firsts or Lasts (or swap the order of the Lasts if it makes a difference!) and repeat.

Example 4.8

Factorise: $x^2 - 10x + 16$

Solution

step 1 $(x\quad 4)(x\quad 4)$

step 2 Outsides: $4x$
Insides: $4x$

step 3 Middle term $-10x$ cannot be made from $4x$ and $4x$

step 1 again $(x\quad 2)(x\quad 8)$

step 2 Outsides: $8x$
Insides: $2x$

step 3 Middle term $-10x$ is $-8x - 2x$

step 4 $\mathbf{(x - 2)(x - 8)}$
and multiplying out gives:
$x^2 - 10x + 16$

Example 4.9

Factorise: $6x^2 + x - 2$

Solution

step 1 $(2x\quad 2)(3x\quad 1)$

step 2 Outsides: $2x$
Insides: $6x$

step 3 Middle term x cannot be made from $2x$ and $6x$

step 1 again $(2x\quad 1)(3x\quad 2)$

step 2 Outsides: $4x$
Insides: $3x$

step 3 Middle term x is $4x - 3x$

step 4 $\mathbf{(2x - 1)(3x + 2)}$
Check this by multiplying out.

Factorising Fully

$$30 = 2 \times 15$$

However, 15 can be factorised further giving: $30 = 2 \times 3 \times 5$

Similarly: $8x^2 - 2y^2$
$= 2(4x^2 - y^2)$

However, $4x^2 - y^2$ can be factorised further because it is a difference of squares, giving:

$$2(2x - y)(2x + y)$$

which is now factorised fully.

Example 4.10

Factorise fully:

(a) $2x^2 - 14x + 24$

(b) $3x^4 - 48$

Solution

(a) $2x^2 - 14x + 24$ common factor 2

$= 2(x^2 - 7x + 12)$ quadratic

$= \mathbf{2(x - 3)(x - 4)}$

(b) $3x^4 - 48$ common factor 3

$= 3(x^4 - 16)$ difference of squares: $(x^2)^2 - 4^2$

$= 3(x^2 - 4)(x^2 + 4)$ difference of squares: $x^2 - 2^2$

$= \mathbf{3(x - 2)(x + 2)(x^2 + 4)}$

5. Circles

Circle Formulae (reminder)

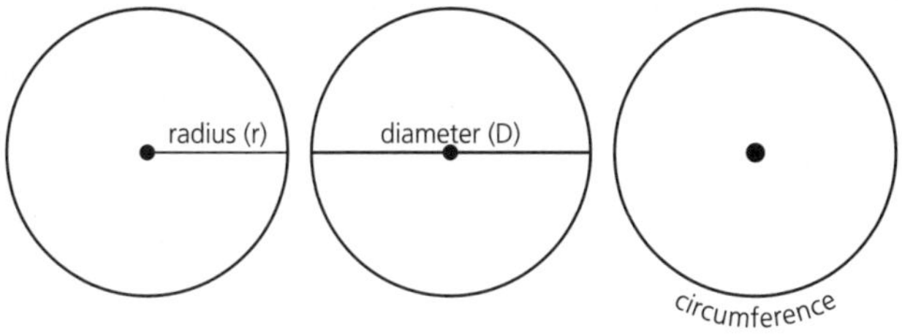

Diameter = 2 × radius (D = 2r)

Circumference = π × diameter (C = πD)
where π = 3·14159…

In calculations, always use the π button on your calculator.

Area of circle = π × radius × radius (A = πr^2)

Finding Arcs and Sectors

A circle with centre O:

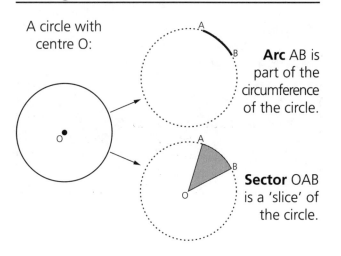

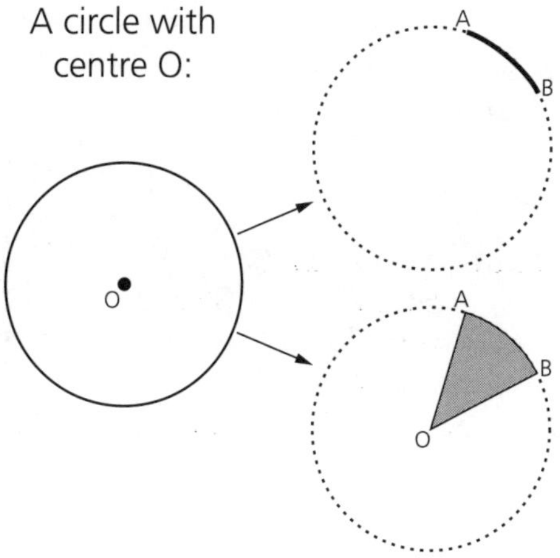

Arc AB is part of the circumference of the circle.

Sector OAB is a 'slice' of the circle.

5. Circles

An example:

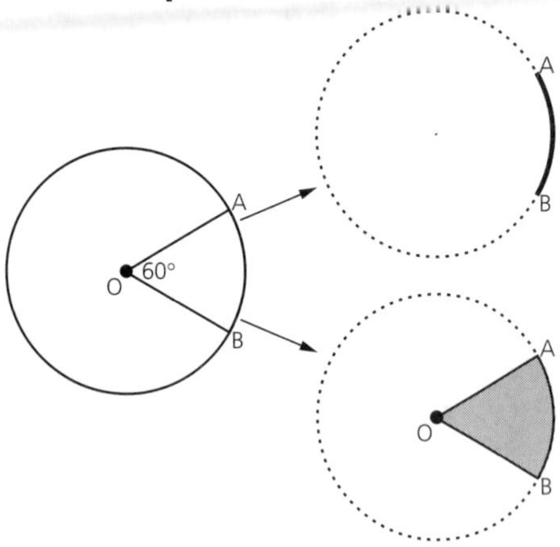

Arc AB = $\frac{1}{6}$ of circumference of circle

Sector OAB = $\frac{1}{6}$ of area of circle

The 'circle fraction' $\frac{1}{6}$ is determined by the 60° angle at the centre. A complete turn is 360° and 60° is $\frac{60}{360} = \frac{1}{6}$ of this complete turn.

In general:

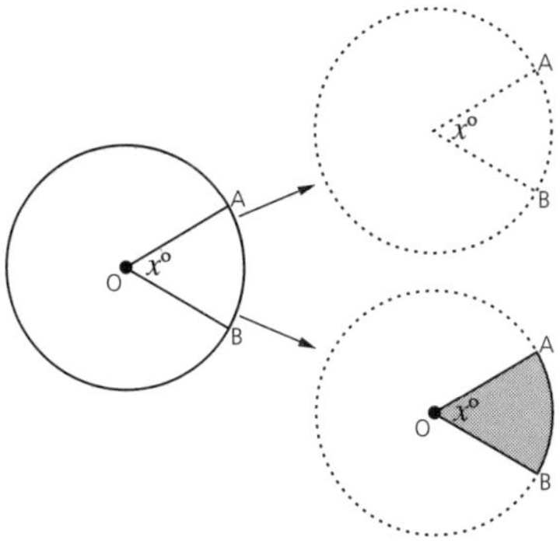

Arc AB = a fraction of circumference of circle

Arc AB = $\frac{x}{360} \times \pi D$

Sector OAB = a fraction of area of circle

Sector OAB = $\frac{x}{360} \times \pi r^2$

Finding the angle at the centre

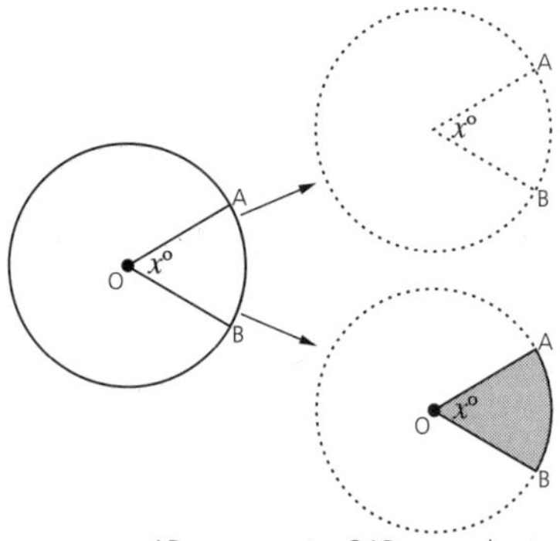

Since arc AB = $\frac{x}{360}$ × circumference

then $\frac{\text{arc AB}}{\text{circumference}} = \frac{x}{360}$

Since sector OAB = $\frac{x}{360}$ × circle area

then $\frac{\text{sector OAB}}{\text{circle area}} = \frac{x}{360}$

So: $\frac{\text{arc AB}}{\text{circumference}} = \frac{\text{sector OAB}}{\text{circle area}} = \frac{\text{angle at centre}}{360}$ = the same circle fraction

What fraction of the circumference is arc AB?

What fraction of the circle area is sector OAB?

What fraction of 360° is the angle at the centre?

All answers are the same 'circle fraction'.

Find this 'circle fraction' to solve 'angle at the centre' problems.

Example 5.1

Find:

(a) The length of arc AB

(b) The area of sector OAB

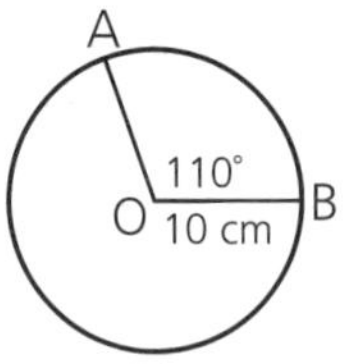

Solution

(a) Arc AB = a fraction of circumference of circle

Arc AB = $\frac{110}{360} \times \pi \times 20$ (diameter)

= 19·198…

≑ **19·2 cm** (to 1 d. p.)

(b) Sector OAB = a fraction of area of circle

Sector OAB = $\frac{110}{360} \times \pi \times 10^2$ (radius)

= 95·993…

≑ **96·0 cm²** (to 1 d. p.)

Example 5.2

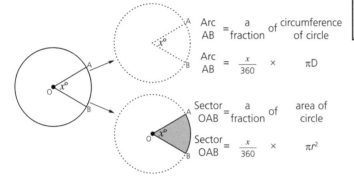

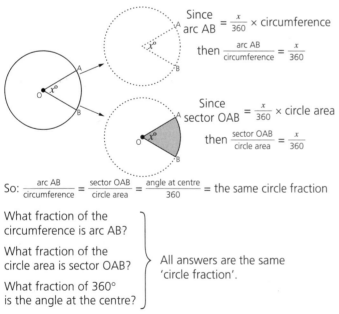

A sector of area 8 m² was removed from a 10 m diameter clock face for repair. Find, to 1 d. p., the angle at the centre of the sector.

Solution

The 'circle fraction' in this case is:

$\frac{\text{sector OAB}}{\text{circle area}} = \frac{8}{\pi \times 5^2} = 0{\cdot}1018\ldots$

(radius)

So angle at centre = circle fraction × 360
= 0·1018… × 360
= 36·66…
≑ **36·7°** (to 1 d. p.)

Pythagoras' Theorem (reminder)

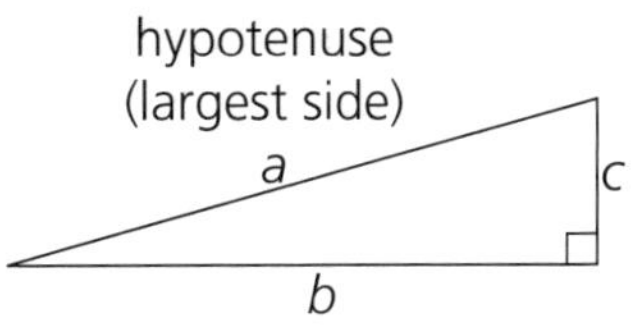

In a right-angled triangle

$$a^2 = b^2 + c^2$$

largest side

or $b^2 = a^2 - c^2$ or $c^2 = a^2 - b^2$

smaller side   smaller side

Note (1)
To find the hypotenuse (largest side), **add** the squares of the smaller sides, then find the square root. (Use [√] button on calculator.)

Note (2)
To find a smaller side, **subtract** the squares of the other side (largest minus smallest), then find the square root. (Use [√] button.)

Tangent Properties

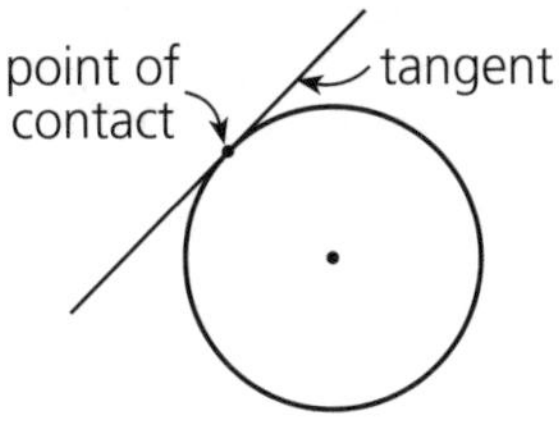

A tangent is a line which touches a circle at only one point. This point is called the **point of contact**.

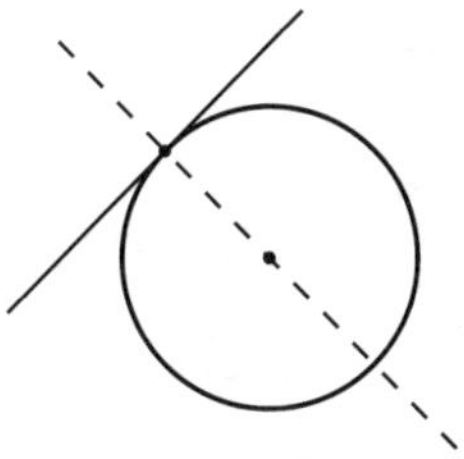

The line through the centre and the point of contact is an axis of symmetry for the diagram.

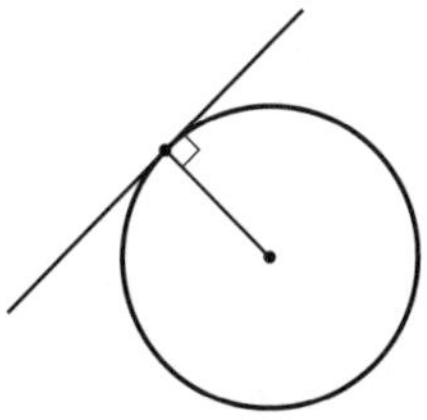

This means that a tangent and the radius to the point of contact are at right angles (perpendicular).

Two tangents can be drawn to a circle from a point outside the circle.

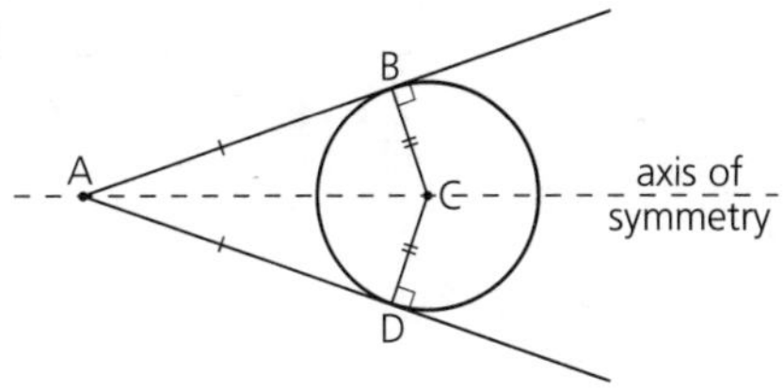

In the diagram, tangents AB and AD and the two radii CB and CD form a kite ABCD.

Example 5.3

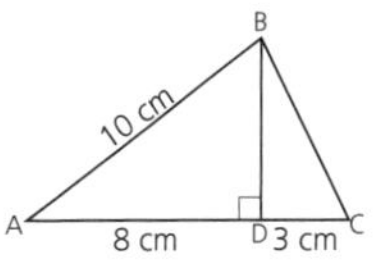

Calculate BC to 1 d. p.

Solution

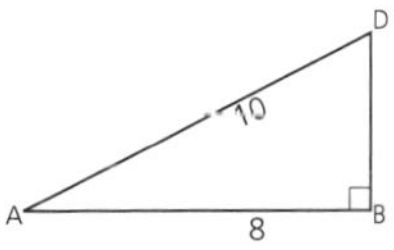

$BD^2 = 10^2 - 8^2$
$= 100 - 64 = 36$

So $BD = \sqrt{36} = 6$

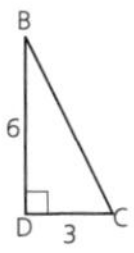

$BC^2 = 6^2 + 3^2$
$= 36 + 9$
$= 45$

So $BC = \sqrt{45} = 6{\cdot}708\ldots$

giving BC ≑ **6·7 cm** (to 1 d. p.)

Example 5.4

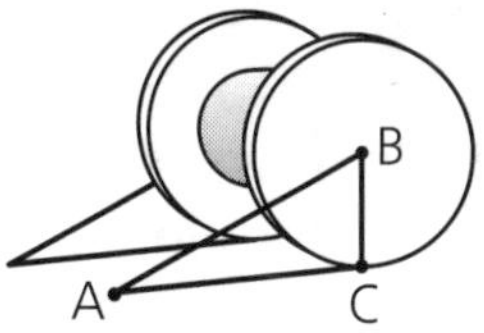

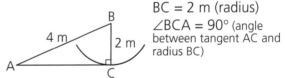

A cylindrical drum of radius 2 m is held in place by triangular metal supports on each side as shown. Rod AB is 4 m long and attached to the centre of the circle B, directly above C. How many triangular metal frames like ABC can be made from a 100 m length of rod?

Solution

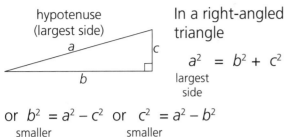

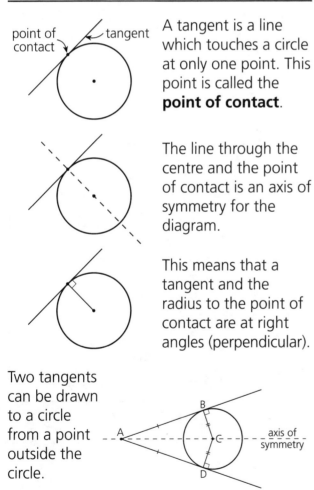

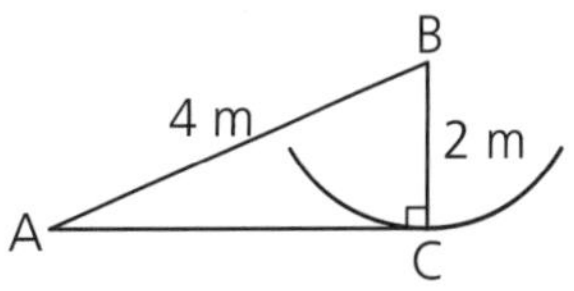

BC = 2 m (radius)
∠BCA = 90° (angle between tangent AC and radius BC)

So $AC^2 = 4^2 - 2^2 = 16 - 4 = 12$
giving $AC = \sqrt{12} = 3{\cdot}46\ldots$

Length of rod in one frame $= 4 + 2 + 3{\cdot}46\ldots$
$= 9{\cdot}46\ldots$

Total no. of frames $= \frac{100}{9{\cdot}46} = 10{\cdot}56\ldots$

10 frames only (Don't round up since 11 frames would require over 100 m of rod.)

Angles in a Semicircle

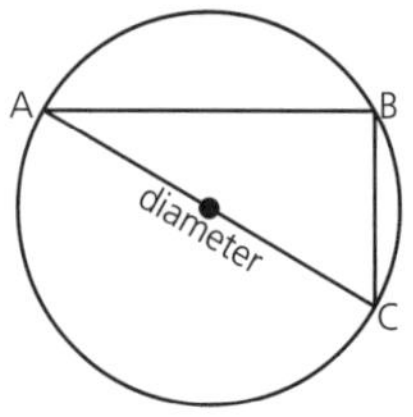

∠ABC is called an angle in a semicircle.

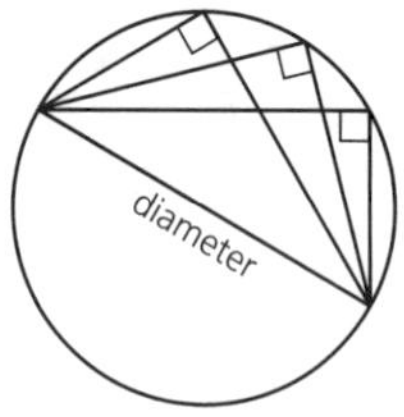

All angles in a semicircle are right-angles (90°).

Example 5.5

In an old semicircular tunnel of diameter 10 m, a roof support AB is 8 m long. Find the length of support CB.

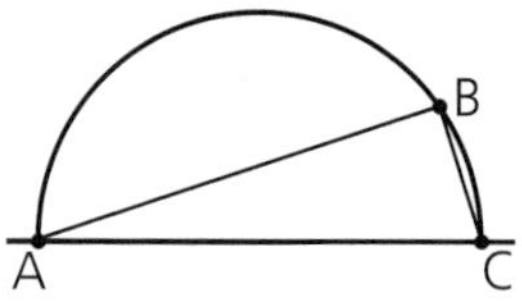

Solution

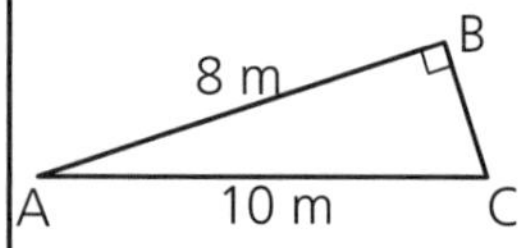

∠ABC = 90°
(It is an angle in a semicircle.)

Using Pythagoras' Theorem gives:

$BC^2 = 10^2 - 8^2 = 100 - 64 = 36$

So $BC = \sqrt{36} = \mathbf{6\ m}$

Symmetry and Chords

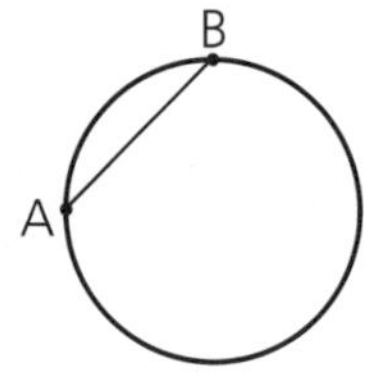

A line joining two points on a circumference is called a chord. The diameter is a special chord that passes through the centre. It is the longest possible chord.

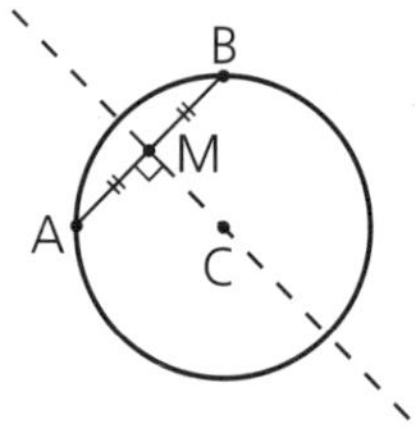

The axis of symmetry of the diagram passes through M, the midpoint of chord AB, and through the centre C. It is perpendicular to chord AB and bisects it (AM = MB).

Example 5.6

A circular table of diameter 1·4 m is hinged to the wall along AB as shown. The table, when up, extends 1·3 m out from the wall. What length of hinge is required?

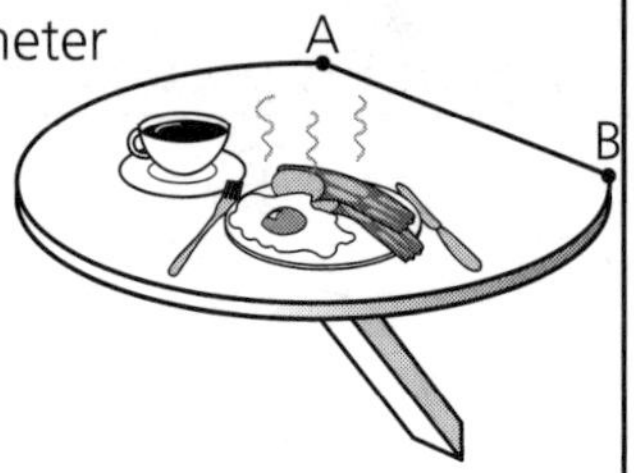

Solution

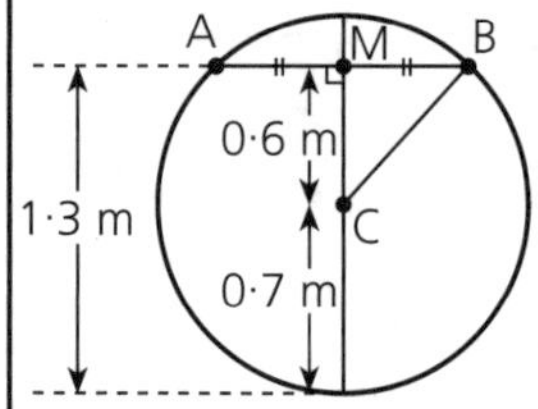

Draw in the diameter perpendicular to chord AB.
M is the midpoint of AB.
MC = 1·3 − 0·7 = 0·6 m
(radius)
CB = 0·7 m (radius)

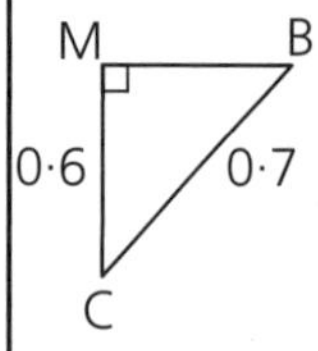

Use Pythagoras' Theorem:
$MB^2 = 0{\cdot}7^2 - 0{\cdot}6^2 = 0{\cdot}13$

So $MB = \sqrt{0{\cdot}13} = 0{\cdot}360\ldots$

giving $AB = 2 \times MB$
$= 2 \times 0{\cdot}360\ldots$
$= 0{\cdot}721\ldots$

The hinge is **72 cm** (to the nearest cm).

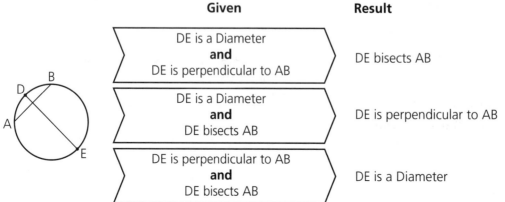

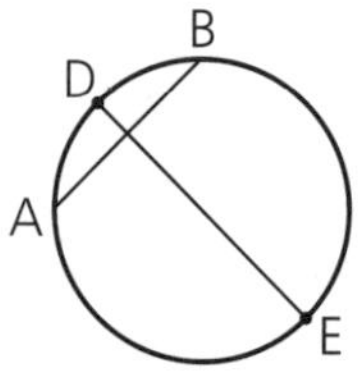

Given	Result
DE is a Diameter **and** DE is perpendicular to AB	DE bisects AB
DE is a Diameter **and** DE bisects AB	DE is perpendicular to AB
DE is perpendicular to AB **and** DE bisects AB	DE is a Diameter

Right-angled Triangles (reminder)

The sides of a right-angled triangle are named from the viewpoint of one of the angles.

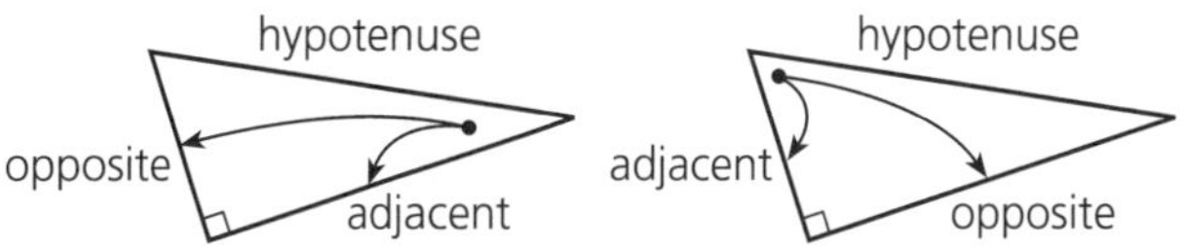

The hypotenuse (the largest side) is always opposite the right-angle.

Reminder

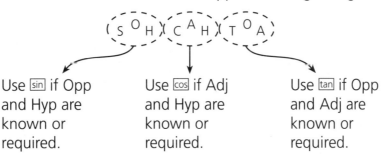

S O H C A H T O A

Use sin if Opp and Hyp are known or required.

Use cos if Adj and Hyp are known or required.

Use tan if Opp and Adj are known or required.

Note

At all times your calculator display should show **D** or **Deg** not **R** or **Rad** or **G** or **Grad**. Otherwise change **Mode** to **Degree**.

Here are three common types of problem.

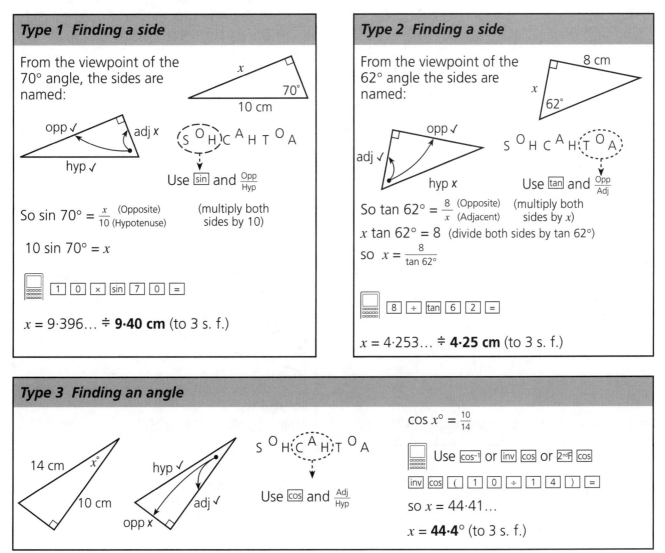

Type 1 Finding a side

From the viewpoint of the 70° angle, the sides are named:

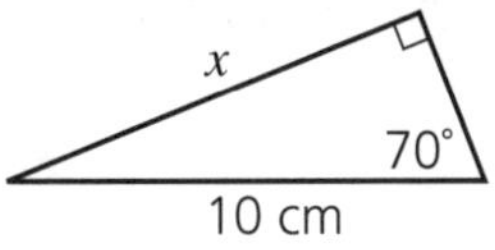

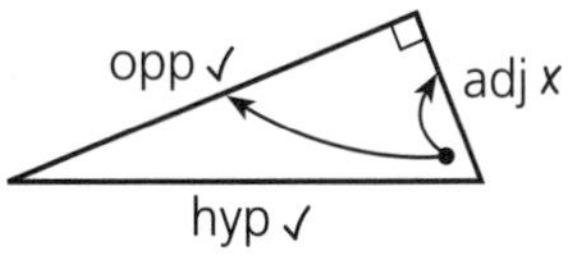

S O H C A H T O A

Use sin and $\frac{\text{Opp}}{\text{Hyp}}$

So $\sin 70° = \frac{x \text{ (Opposite)}}{10 \text{ (Hypotenuse)}}$ (multiply both sides by 10)

$10 \sin 70° = x$

1 0 × sin 7 0 =

$x = 9{\cdot}396\ldots \doteqdot$ **9·40 cm** (to 3 s. f.)

Type 2 Finding a side

From the viewpoint of the 62° angle the sides are named:

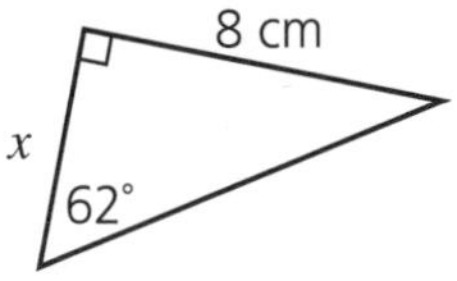

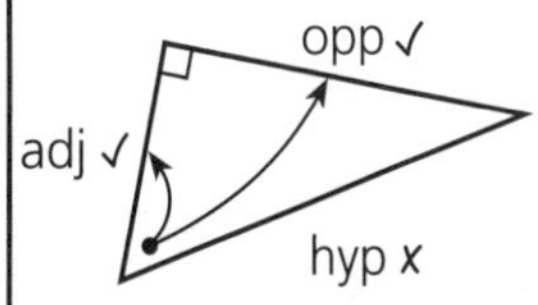

S O H C A H T O A

Use tan and $\frac{\text{Opp}}{\text{Adj}}$

So $\tan 62° = \frac{8 \text{ (Opposite)}}{x \text{ (Adjacent)}}$ (multiply both sides by x)

$x \tan 62° = 8$ (divide both sides by tan 62°)

so $x = \frac{8}{\tan 62°}$

8 ÷ tan 6 2 =

$x = 4{\cdot}253\ldots \doteqdot$ **4·25 cm** (to 3 s. f.)

Type 3 Finding an angle

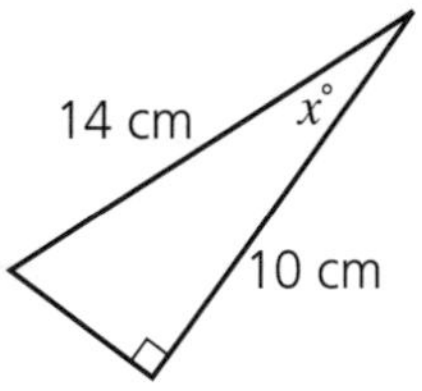

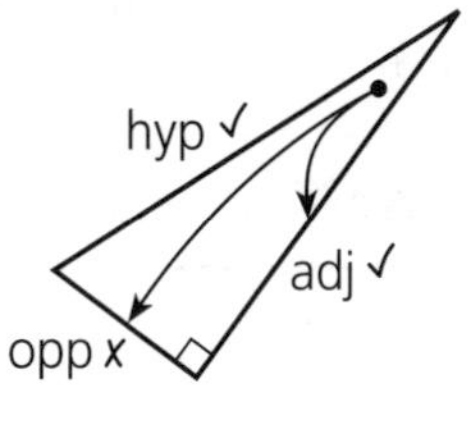

S O H C A H T O A

Use cos and $\frac{\text{Adj}}{\text{Hyp}}$

$\cos x° = \frac{10}{14}$

Use $\cos^{-1}$ or inv cos or 2ndF cos

inv cos (1 0 ÷ 1 4) =

so $x = 44{\cdot}41\ldots$

$x =$ **44·4°** (to 3 s. f.)

Angles greater than 90°

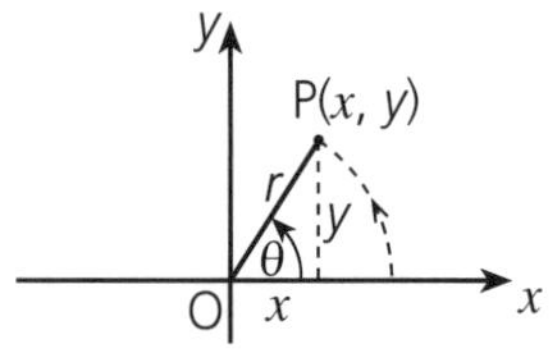

OP rotates about O from the x-axis by θ°.
$\sin\theta = \frac{y}{r}$ $\cos\theta = \frac{x}{r}$
$\tan\theta = \frac{y}{x}$
(Using $S^{O}H C^{A}H T^{O}A$)

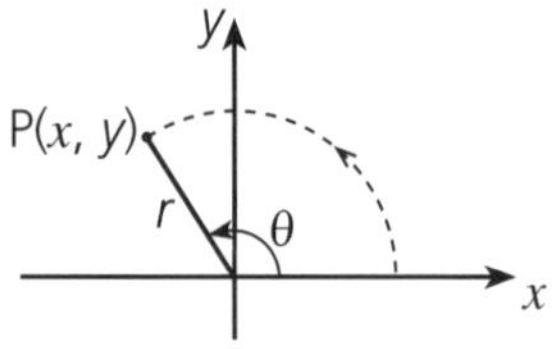

When θ° becomes greater than 90° then:
$\sin\theta = \frac{y}{r}$ $\cos\theta = \frac{x}{r}$ $\tan\theta = \frac{y}{x}$
can still be used to calculate the values of $\sin\theta$, $\cos\theta$ and $\tan\theta$.

Example 6.1

Use your calculator to find the following to 3 s. f.
(a) sin 23°
(b) cos 123°
(c) tan 224°

Solution
(a) sin 23° = 0·3907… ≑ **0·391** (to 3 s. f.)
(b) cos 123° = –0·5446… ≑ **–0·545** (to 3 s. f.)
(c) tan 224° = 0·9656… ≑ **0·966** (to 3 s. f.)

Naming the sides of a triangle

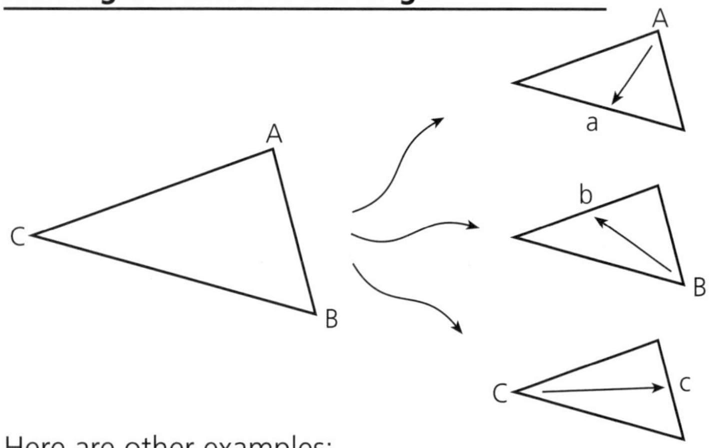

The small letters used for the sides match the capital letters used for the opposite angles as shown in this diagram.

Here are other examples:

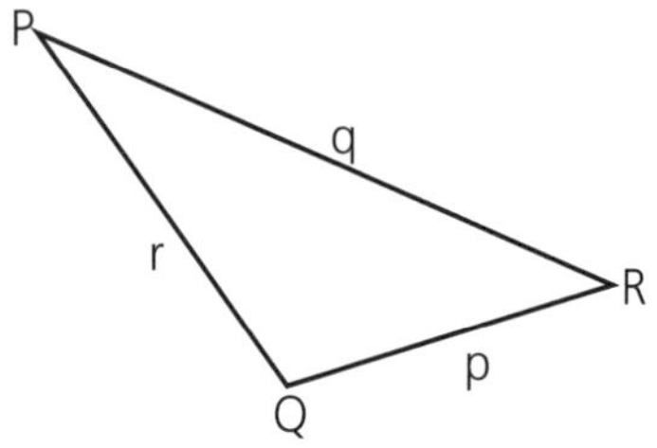

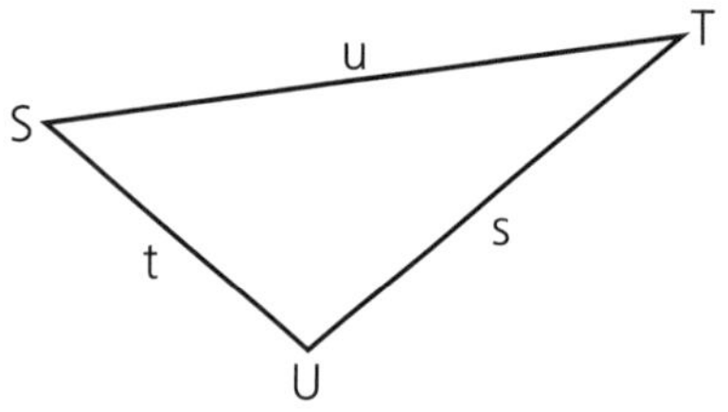

Area of a Triangle

If the triangle is right-angled:
Area = $\frac{1}{2}bh$

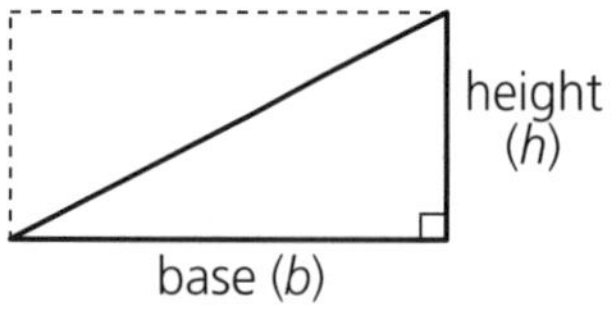

If you know the height: Area = $\frac{1}{2}bh$

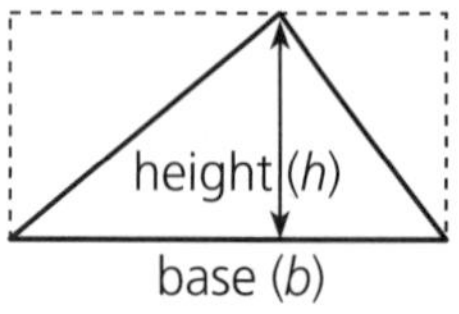

If you know two sides and the angle included between these sides:

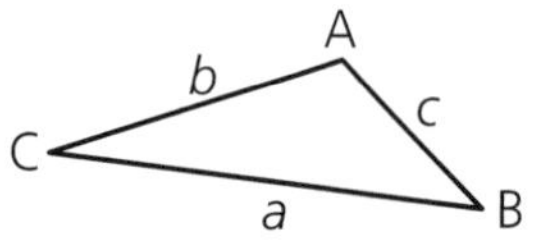

Area = $\frac{1}{2}ab \sin C$ or $\frac{1}{2}ac \sin B$ or $\frac{1}{2}bc \sin A$.

Example 6.2

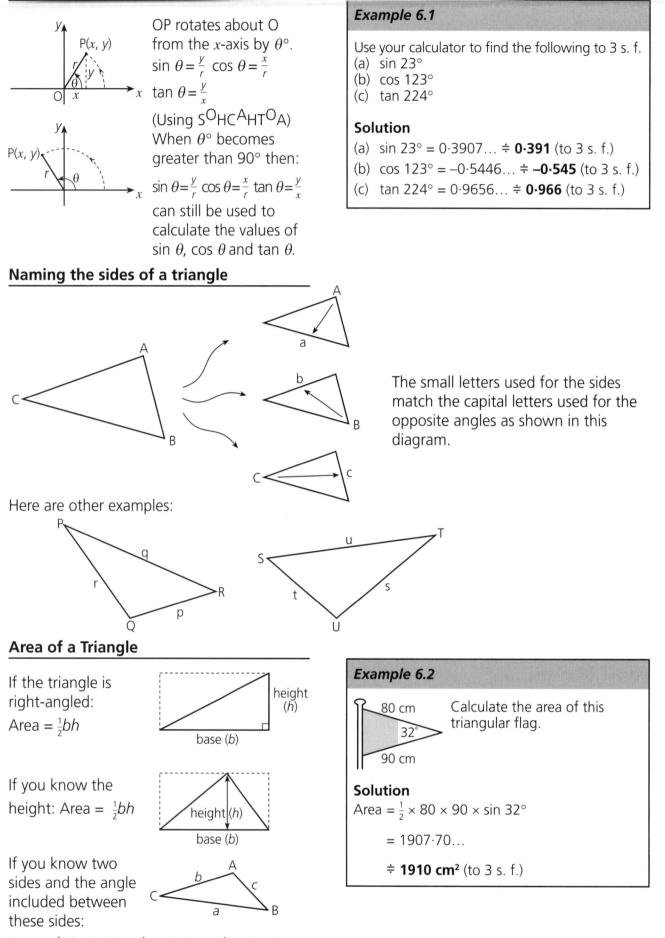

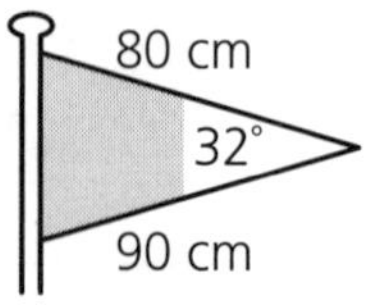

Calculate the area of this triangular flag.

Solution
Area = $\frac{1}{2} \times 80 \times 90 \times \sin 32°$
= 1907·70…
≑ **1910 cm²** (to 3 s. f.)

The Sine Rule

In **any** triangle ABC:

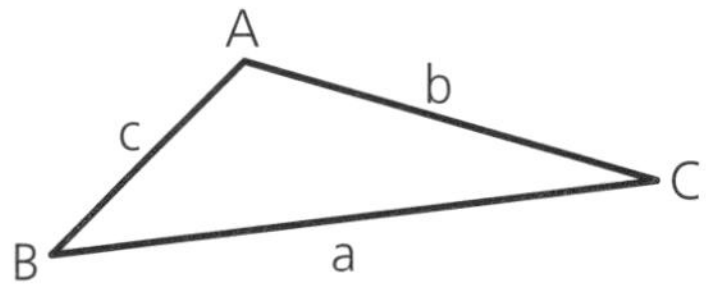

$$\frac{a}{\sin A} = \frac{b}{\sin B} = \frac{c}{\sin C}$$ (the **sine rule**)

How do you know when to use the sine rule?

Your problem will involve two pairs of 'opposites':

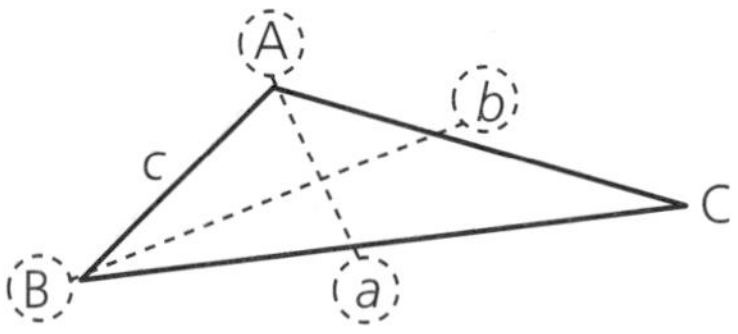

If any three of ∠A, ∠B, a and b are known then the fourth can be calculated using the **sine rule**.

Example 6.3

Calculate PR in triangle PQR.

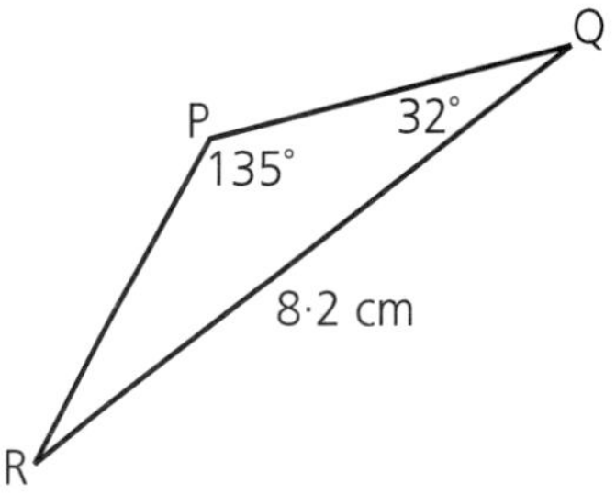

Solution

The sine rule in triangle PQR is

$$\frac{p✓}{\sin P✓} = \frac{q}{\sin Q✓} = \frac{r}{\sin R}$$

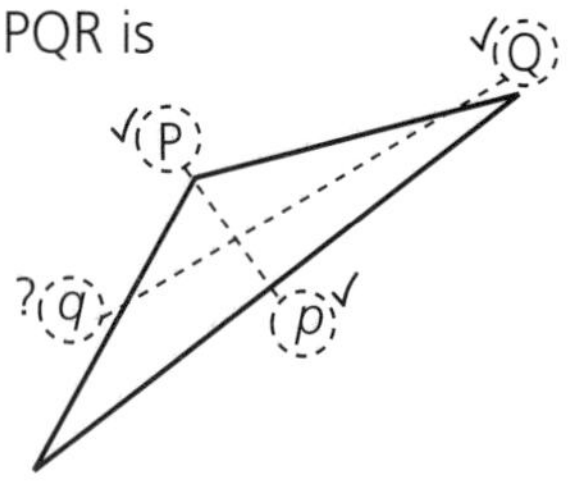

Use

$$\frac{q}{\sin Q} = \frac{p}{\sin P}$$

giving $\frac{q}{\sin 32°} = \frac{8·2}{\sin 135°}$

(multiply both sides by sin 32°)

So $q = \frac{8·2 \times \sin 32°}{\sin 135°} = 6·145...$

≑ **6·15** (to 3 s. f.)

Example 6.4

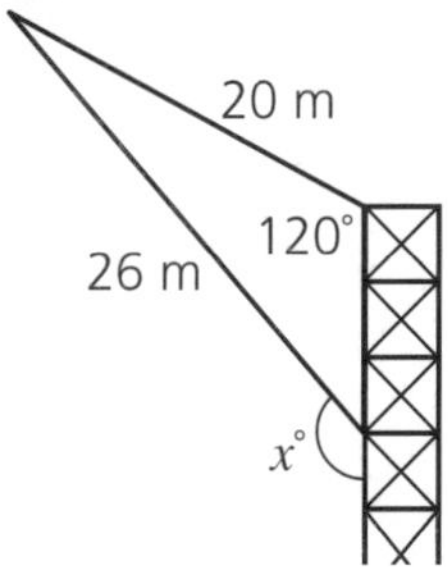

The 20 m top support on a crane jib makes a 120° angle with the main tower of the crane as shown in the diagram. What angle does the 26 m lower support on the crane jib make with the tower?

Solution

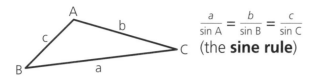

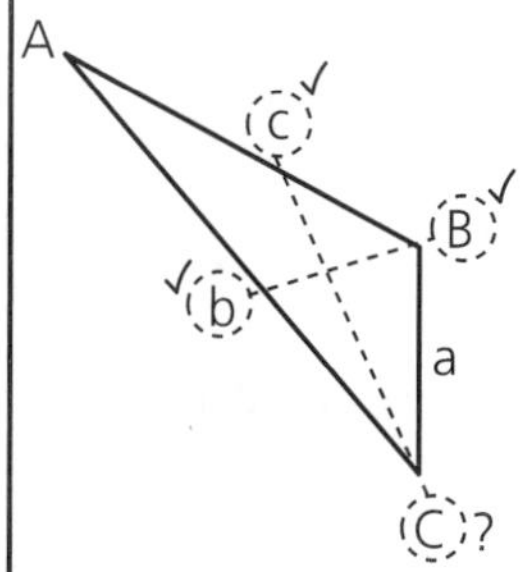

The sine rule in triangle ABC is $\frac{a}{\sin A} = \frac{b}{\sin B} = \frac{c}{\sin C}$

In this case use: $\frac{b}{\sin B} = \frac{c}{\sin C}$ giving

$\frac{26}{\sin 120°} = \frac{20}{\sin C}$ (multiply both sides by sin C)

$\Rightarrow \frac{26 \sin C}{\sin 120°} = 20$ (multiply both sides by sin 120°)

$\Rightarrow 26 \sin C = 20 \sin 120°$ (divide both sides by 26)

$\Rightarrow \sin C = \frac{20 \sin 120°}{26} = 0·6661...$ (now use [sin⁻¹] or [inv] [sin] or [2ndF] [sin])

∠C = 41·77...°

∠C ≑ 41·8°   So $x°$ = 180° – 41·8° = **138·2°**

The Cosine Rule (finding a side)

In **any** triangle ABC

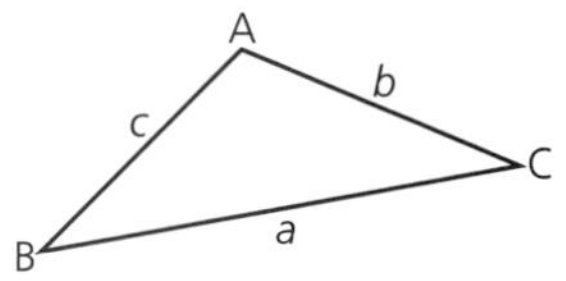

$a^2 = b^2 + c^2 - 2bc \cos A$
or
$b^2 = a^2 + c^2 - 2ac \cos B$
or
$c^2 = b^2 + a^2 - 2ba \cos C$
(the **cosine rule**)

How do you know when to use the cosine rule? Your problem will involve knowing two sides and the angle included between these sides: If you know the two sides and the included angle you can find the side opposite this angle.

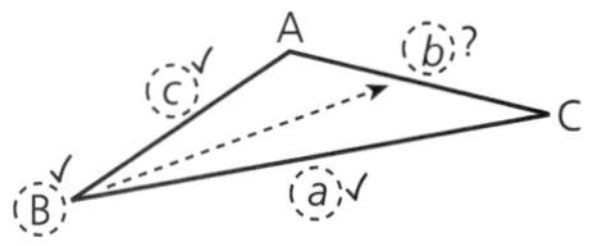

(In this case use:
$b^2 = a^2 + c^2 - 2ac \cos B$

Example 6.5

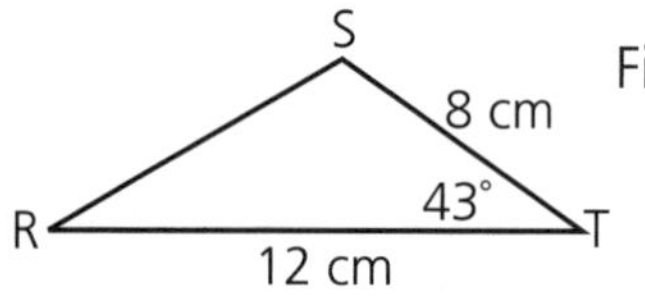

Find RS.

Solution:

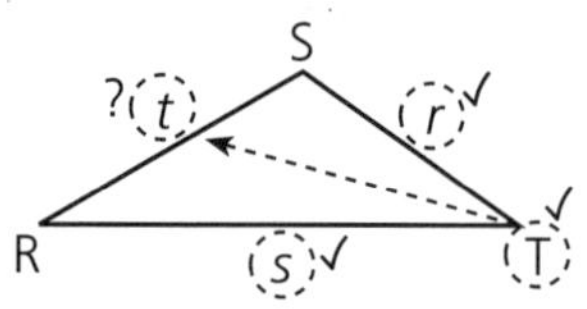

Use $t^2 = r^2 + s^2 - 2rs \cos T$
$t^2 = 8^2 + 12^2 - 2 \times 8 \times 12 \times \cos 43°$
Most calculators will correctly calculate this as follows:
[8] [x^2] [+] [1] [2] [x^2] [−] [2] [×] [8] [×] [1] [2] [×] [cos] [4] [3] [=]
giving
$t^2 = 67{\cdot}58\ldots$ (take the square root of both sides)
so $t = \sqrt{67{\cdot}58\ldots} = 8{\cdot}220\ldots \doteqdot$ **8·22cm (to 3 s. f.)**

The Cosine Rule (finding an angle)

The cosine rule has another form:
In **any** triangle ABC

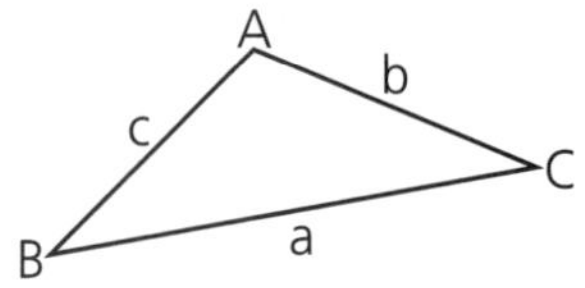

$$\cos A = \frac{b^2 + c^2 - a^2}{2bc}$$

or

$$\cos B = \frac{a^2 + c^2 - b^2}{2ac}$$

or

$$\cos C = \frac{a^2 + b^2 - c^2}{2ab}$$

This form of the cosine rule allows you to find an angle if you know all three sides.

Example 6.6

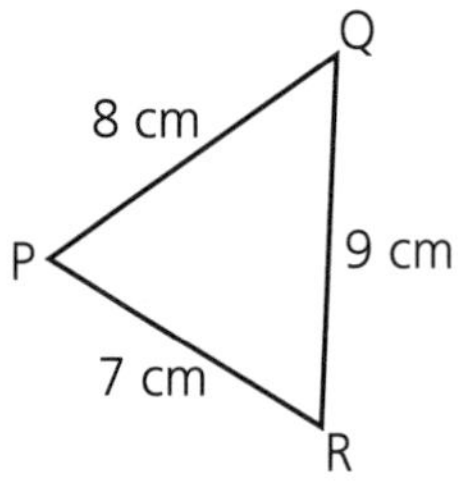

Calculate the size of angle PQR.

Solution:
Use

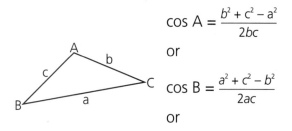

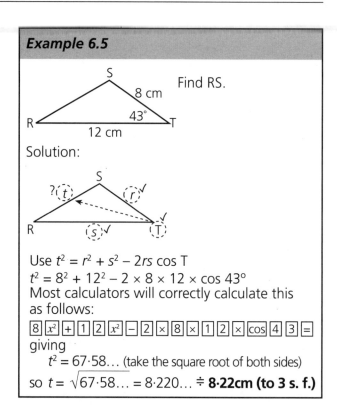

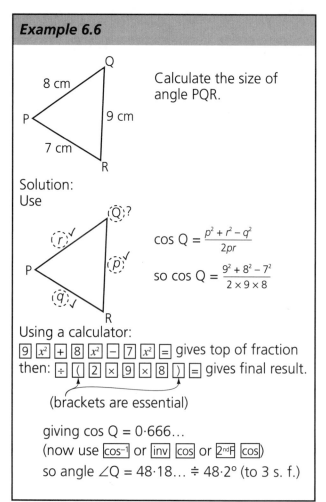

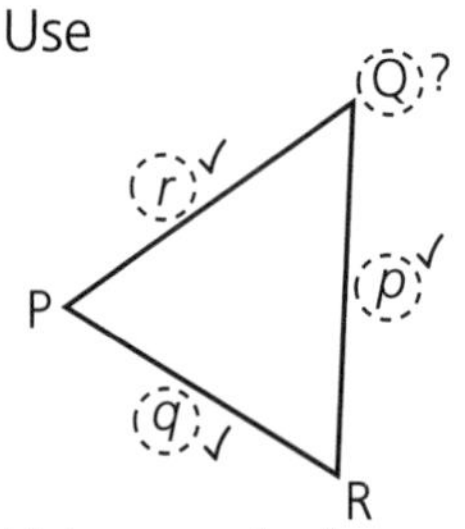

$$\cos Q = \frac{p^2 + r^2 - q^2}{2pr}$$

$$\text{so } \cos Q = \frac{9^2 + 8^2 - 7^2}{2 \times 9 \times 8}$$

Using a calculator:
[9] [x^2] [+] [8] [x^2] [−] [7] [x^2] [=] gives top of fraction
then: [÷] [(] [2] [×] [9] [×] [8] [)] [=] gives final result.
(brackets are essential)

giving $\cos Q = 0{\cdot}666\ldots$
(now use [$\cos^{-1}$] or [inv] [cos] or [2ndF] [cos])
so angle $\angle Q = 48{\cdot}18\ldots \doteqdot 48{\cdot}2°$ (to 3 s. f.)

Setting up a Linear Equation

Two adults and three children go to the cinema. Their tickets cost £13 in total. If the price of an adult and a child's ticket are not known then letters are used:

Child's ticket: £x Adult's ticket: £y

Total cost is £$3x + 2y$

3 lots of £x 2 lots of £y

So $3x + 2y = 13$ (a linear equation)

Example 7.1

The total cost of my journey one day was £15. The bus cost 30p per km and the taxi charged 50p per km. Set up a linear equation for this situation.

Solution

Distance travelled by bus: b km
Distance travelled by taxi: t km

Cost: $30b + 50t$ pence
or £$(0{\cdot}3b + 0{\cdot}5t)$
so $0{\cdot}3b + 0{\cdot}5t = 15$

Solving Problems Graphically

Three burgers and two pizzas cost £12.
Using letters: 1 burger costs £x
1 pizza costs £y
Giving a total cost of £$(3x + 2y)$
So $3x + 2y = 12$
This linear equation can be graphed as shown in the diagram opposite.

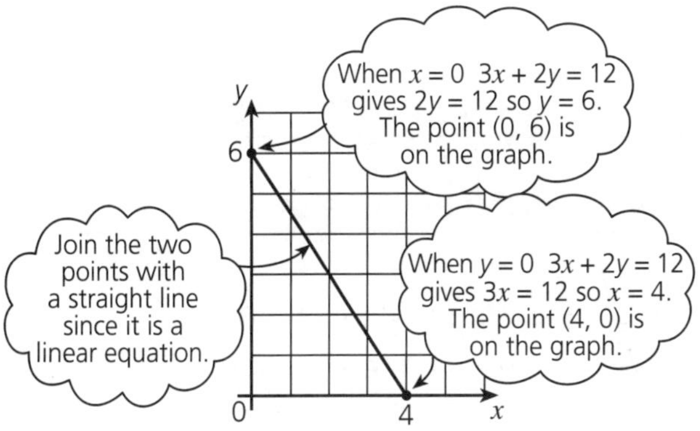

When $x = 0$ $3x + 2y = 12$ gives $2y = 12$ so $y = 6$. The point (0, 6) is on the graph.
Join the two points with a straight line since it is a linear equation.
When $y = 0$ $3x + 2y = 12$ gives $3x = 12$ so $x = 4$. The point (4, 0) is on the graph.
y
6
0
4
x

If you also know that one burger and one pizza together cost £5 then:
Using letters: $x + y = 5$
The graph of this linear equation can be added to the diagram as shown.

The two lines intersect at (2, 3) giving $x = 2$ and $y = 3$ as the only pair of values for x and y that satisfy both equations simultaneously.

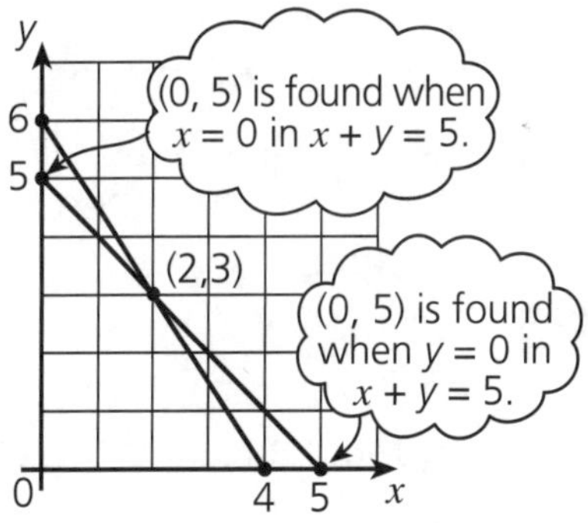

(0, 5) is found when $x = 0$ in $x + y = 5$.

(0, 5) is found when $y = 0$ in $x + y = 5$.

Thus a burger costs £2 and a pizza costs £3
($x = 2$) ($y = 3$)

Example 7.2

On the first day of my holiday I walked for 2 hours and cycled for 1 hour, covering 10 km that day. On my second day I walked for 1 hour and cycled for 2 hours, covering 14 km that day. I plan to walk 3 hours and cycle 3 hours on day three. How far will I cover?

Solution

Cycling speed: x km/hr. Walking speed: y km/hr.

1st day:	$2y$ +	x	=	10
	(2 hours at y km/hr)	(1 hour at x km/hr)		(10 km covered)
2nd day:	y +	$2x$	=	14
	(1 hour at y km/hr)	(2 hours at x km/hr)		(14 km covered)

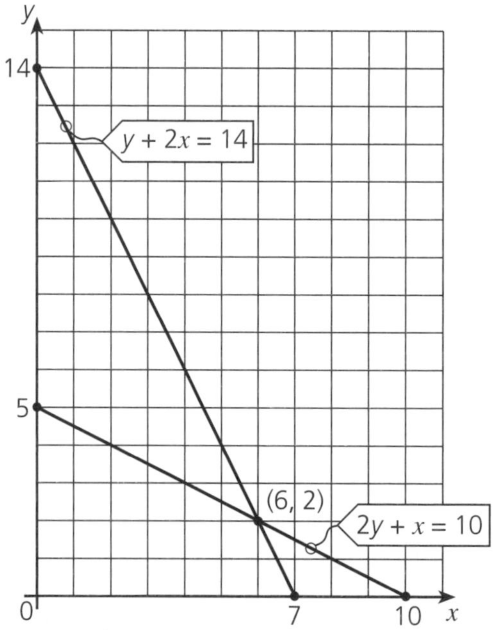

From the graph the point of intersection is (6, 2) giving $x = 6$ and y = 2.
So I cycle at 6 km/hr and walk at 2km/hr.
On day 3: 3 hours cycling gives $3 \times 6 = 18$ km and 3 hours walking gives $3 \times 2 = 6$ km
i.e. $3x + 3y = 3 \times 6 + 3 \times 2 = 18 + 6 = 24$ km. I would expect to cover **24 km** on Day 3.

Solving Problems Algebraically

The general method is as follows:

step 1 Rearrange the equations (if necessary) to get the letters lined up.

step 2 Multiply the equations with the aim of matching the number of one of the letters in each equation.

step 3 Add or subtract to eliminate the matching letter then solve the resulting equation.

step 4 Put the value you found in Step 3 back into one of the original equations to find the value of the other letter.

Example 7.3

Solve $\left.\begin{array}{l} 2x = 7 - 3y \\ 3x - 2y = 4 \end{array}\right\}$

Solution

step 1 Rearrange the 1st equation:

$$\left.\begin{array}{rcl} 2x + 3y &=& 7 \\ 3x - 2y &=& 4 \end{array}\right\}$$

(x's and y's are now lined up)

step 2 Let's match the x's:

$$\left.\begin{array}{rcl} 2x + 3y &=& 7 \\ 3x - 2y &=& 4 \end{array}\right. \begin{array}{l} \times 3 \\ \times 2 \end{array}$$

This gives:

$$\left.\begin{array}{rcl} 6x + 9y &=& 21 \\ 6x - 4y &=& 8 \end{array}\right\}$$

(The number of x's match in each equation)

step 3

$$\left.\begin{array}{rcl} 6x + 9y &=& 21 \\ 6x - 4y &=& 8 \end{array}\right\}$$

Subtract:

$$13y = 13$$

$$\text{So } y = 1$$

(Subtract −4 same as adding 4)

step 4 Put $y = 1$ into $2x + 3y = 7$ giving

$2x + 3 = 7$
so $2x = 4$
so $x = 2$

The solution is $\boldsymbol{x = 2}$ and $\boldsymbol{y = 1}$

Example 7.4

A music station on the radio allows a fixed length of time for singles tracks and a longer fixed time for album tracks. One of the DJs knows that in his 35-minute program he can fit 3 album tracks and 5 singles tracks. He also knows that the time allocated for 7 singles tracks is 18 minutes more than the time allocated for 2 album tracks.

Tomorrow he is broadcasting a half-hour program and plans to play 3 album tracks and 4 singles tracks. Will he manage this?

Solution

The time allocated for 1 album track: a minutes
The time allocated for 1 singles track: s minutes

So $3a + 5s = 35$ (3 album tracks and 5 singles tracks in a 35-minute program)
Also $7s = 2a + 18$ (7 singles tracks are 18 minutes longer than 2 album tracks)

This gives:

step 1
$$\left.\begin{aligned} 5s + 3a &= 35 \\ 7s - 2a &= 18 \end{aligned}\right\}$$

step 2
$$\left.\begin{aligned} 5s + 3a &= 35 \\ 7s - 2a &= 18 \end{aligned}\right\} \begin{aligned} \times 2 &\longrightarrow 10s + 6a = 70 \\ \times 3 &\longrightarrow 21s - 6a = 54 \end{aligned}$$

step 3
$$\left.\begin{aligned} 10s + 6a &= 70 \\ 21s - 6a &= 54 \end{aligned}\right\}$$
Add: $31s = 124$
So $s = 4$

step 4
Put $s = 4$ in $5s + 3a = 35$
giving $20 + 3a = 35$ so $3a = 15$
so $a = 5$
album track: 5 minutes singles track: 4 minutes

His plan needs $3a + 4s = 3 \times 5 + 4 \times 4 = 15 + 16 = 31$ minutes, 1 minute too long!

8. Graphs, Charts and Tables

Types of Graphs (reminders)

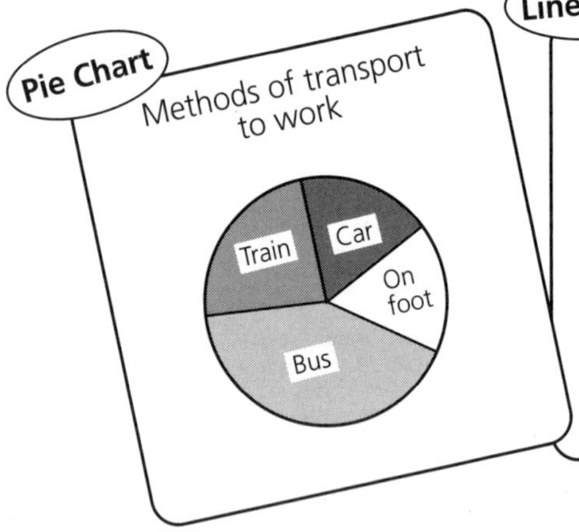

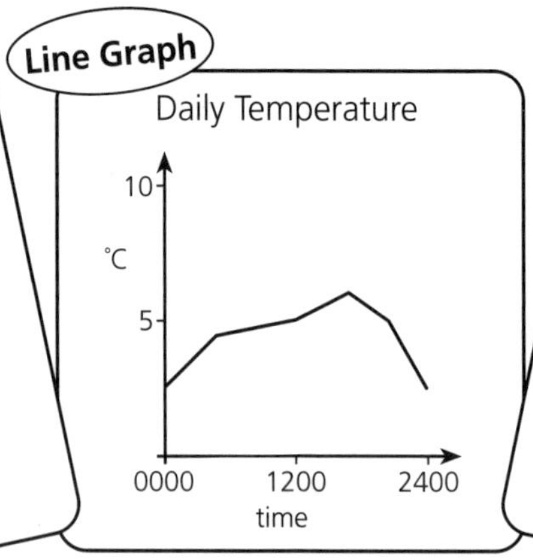

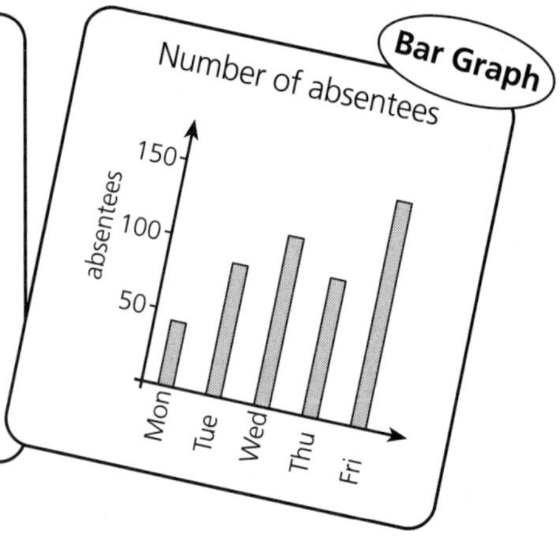

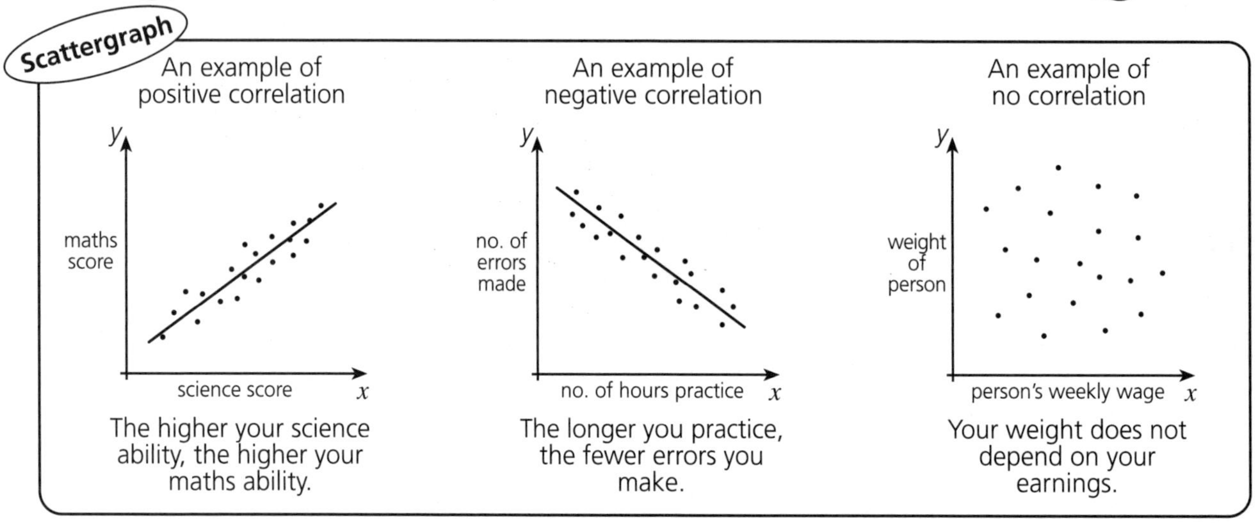

Stem-and-leaf diagram

% Maths Scores

3	4
4	2 4 4 8
5	1
6	6 8
7	0 0 1 7 8
8	1 6

$n = 15$ 4|2 represents a score of 42%

This type of diagram displays a graph of the data set using the actual numbers in the data set. It is a useful method of sorting the data into order when calculating the median and quartiles.

Data set: (% scores in a maths test)

70%, 44%, 42%, 78%, 48%, 44%, 70%, 34%, 81%, 51%, 68%, 86%, 66%, 71%, 77%

Pie Charts (an introduction)

In a **pie chart** all the data set is represented by a complete circle (the 'pie'). Each data value is represented by a sector of the circle (a 'slice of the pie').

The angle at the centre holds the key to all calculations concerning pie charts.

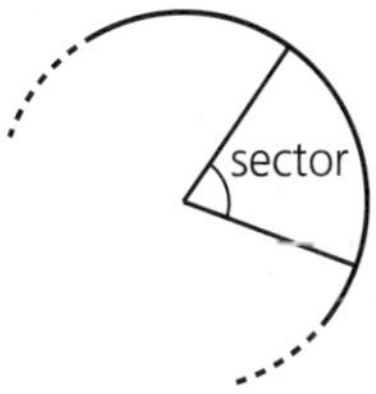

Since a complete circle requires 360° at the centre, the crucial fraction is: $\frac{\text{angle of sector}}{360}$

This gives the fraction of the data contained in that sector.

Constructing Pie Charts

step 1 Draw out a table showing each category of data along with its frequency.

step 2 Calculate the 'Circle Fraction' for each category.

step 3 Calculate the sector angle for each category using the 'Circle Fraction' of step 2 by calculating this fraction of 360°.

step 4 Use a protractor and the sector angles from Step 3 to construct the Pie Chart.

Note

Remember to add a title to your Pie Chart and also state what the full circle represents.

Example 8.1

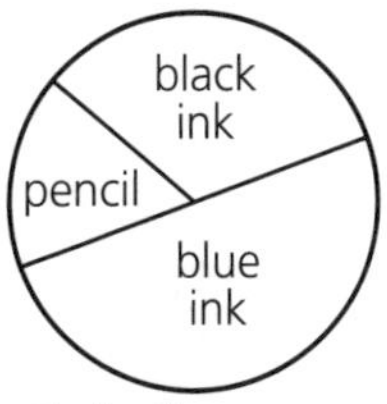

30 students in class were asked what they were using to write their notes.
How many were using ink?

Solution

Measure the angles at the centre with a protractor.

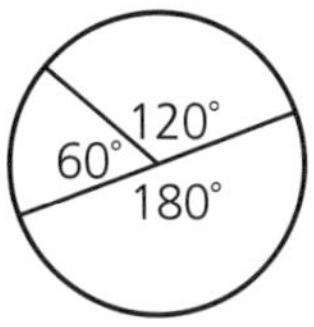

$\frac{60}{360}$ ← angle for 'pencil' (60); complete circle angle (360)

This reduces to $\frac{1}{6}$

No. using pencil = $\frac{1}{6} \times 30 = 5$

So **25** were using ink (black or blue).

Example 8.2

30 commuters were asked the purpose of their journey. 13 said 'work', 12 were 'shopping', 3 'holiday' and 2 said 'visiting a friend'.
Construct a pie chart to show this information.

Solution

Here is a frequency table:

Purpose	Frequency	Fraction	Sector Angle
Work	13	$\frac{13}{30}$	$\frac{13}{30} \times 360 = 156°$
Shopping	12	$\frac{12}{30}$	$\frac{12}{30} \times 360 = 144°$
Holiday	3	$\frac{3}{30}$	$\frac{3}{30} \times 360 = 36°$
Visiting	2	$\frac{2}{30}$	$\frac{2}{30} \times 360 = 24°$

Purpose of Journey

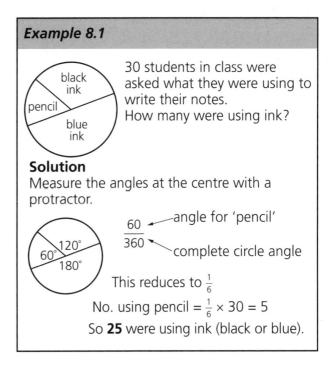

A full circle represents 30 commuters.

Cumulative Frequency

In a frequency table, it can be useful to keep a 'running total' of all the frequencies up to and including a given value.
Questions such as 'How many scored less than 45?' or 'How many were under 5 metres tall?' can then easily be answered using this **cumulative frequency column**.

Example 8.3

Five coins were thrown 20 times and the number of heads at each throw recorded:

2, 3, 2, 4, 2, 3, 1, 4, 2, 1,
4, 2, 0, 2, 3, 5, 3, 3, 2, 1.

(a) Construct a frequency table from this data and add a cumulative frequency column.
(b) In what % of throws were there 3 or fewer heads?

Solution

(a)

No of heads	Frequency	Cumulative Frequency
0	1	1
1	3	4
2	7	11
3	5	16
4	3	19
5	1	20

(b) 16 out of 20 throws gave 3 or fewer heads:
$\frac{16}{20} \times 100\%$ = **80%** of the throws.

Dotplots

Dotplots display each data value as a 'dot' above a numberline. This gives a useful indication of how the values in the data are distributed.

Example 8.4

A golfer records his scores over his last 15 games:

82, 91, 83, 82, 84,
78, 78, 85, 84, 77,
90, 85, 84, 85, 86.

Construct a dotplot from this data set and state his best score, worst score and middle score (median).

Solution

Golf scores

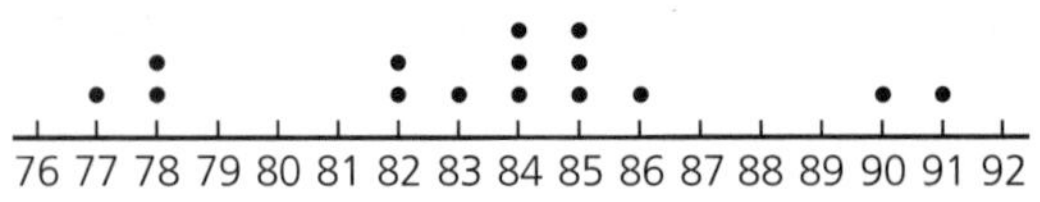

His best score was **77** and his worst was **91**.
His median (middle) score was **84** (8th score in order).

Quartiles

If a data set is arranged in order (smallest to largest) and written as a list on a piece of tape, the tape can be cut into four equal pieces:

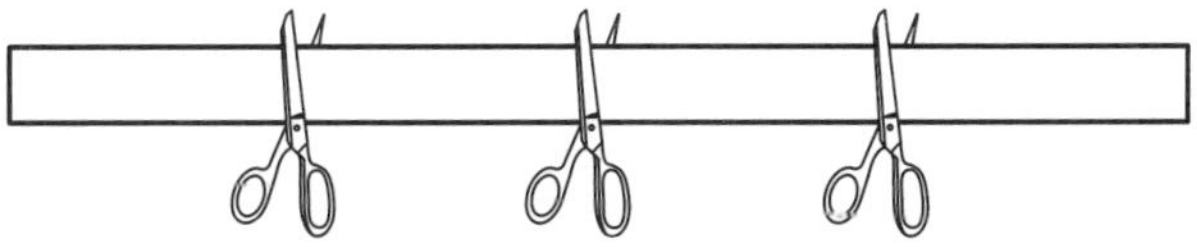

The values in the data set at the places where the tape is cut have names:

Sometimes there may be no value at the cut:

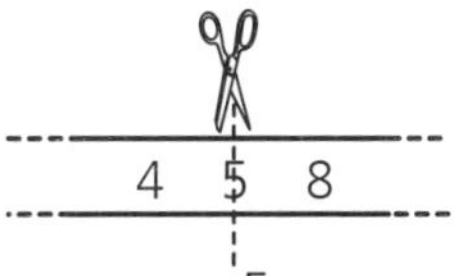

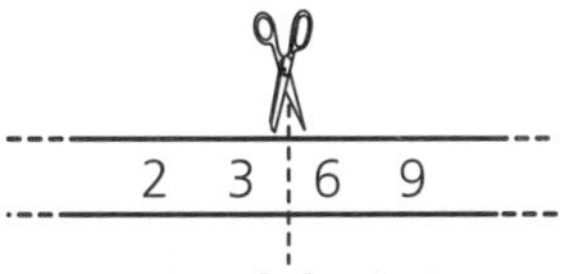

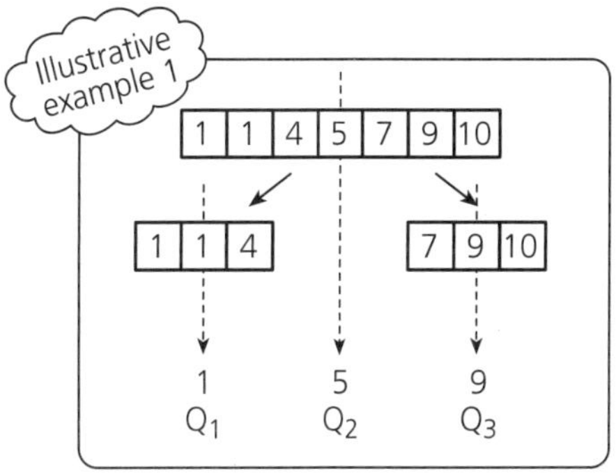

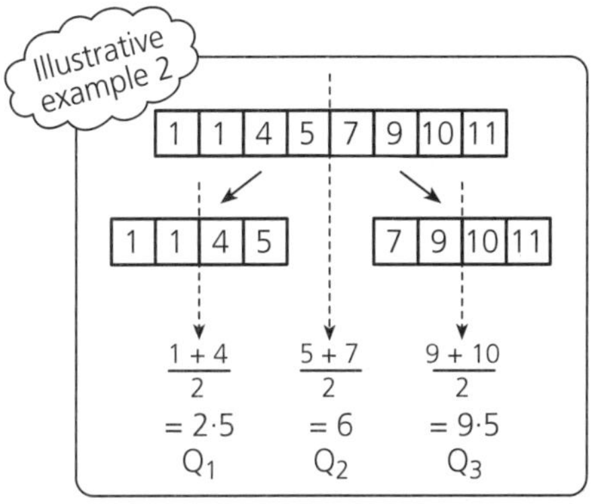

Example 8.5

A researcher counted the number of trips 17 marked bees made during the course of one day to collect nectar:

2, 3, 3, 1, 7, 2,
11, 12, 11, 6, 5, 11,
3, 7, 6, 8, 5.

Calculate the Median and the Upper and Lower Quartiles for this data set.

Solution

The data in order gives:

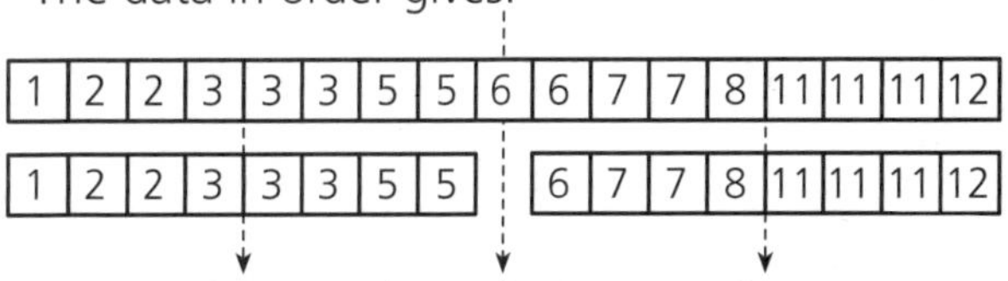

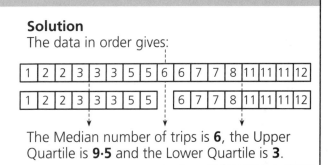

The Median number of trips is **6**, the Upper Quartile is **9·5** and the Lower Quartile is **3**.

Boxplots

Boxplots are an effective way to illustrate the greatest and least values from a data set, along with its Median and Upper and Lower Quartiles:

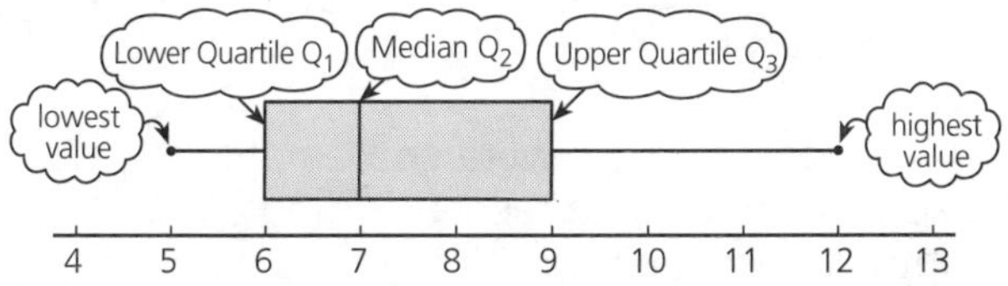

The 'box' stretches from Q_1 to Q_3 (6 to 9), with a line indicating the Median (7). 'Whiskers' extend to the lowest value (5) and to the highest value (12), indicating that the **range** is 7 (12 – 5 = 7).

Example 8.6

Construct a boxplot for this data set:
Midday temperatures (°C) for 2 weeks

3, 8, 9, 7, 7, 5, 11,
12, 12, 12, 13, 9, 7, 7.

Solution

Least: 3 Q_1: 7 Q_2: 8·5 Q_3: 12
Greatest: 13

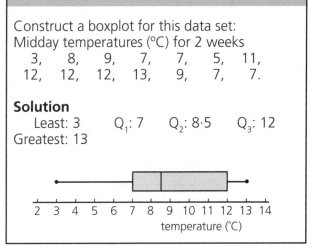

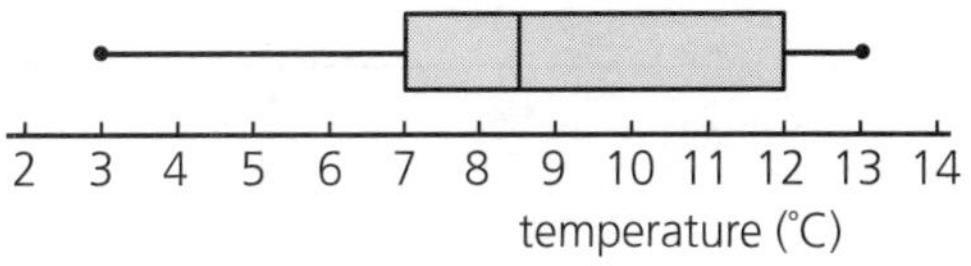

Averages and the Range (reminders)

For the data set: 2, 3, 1, 3, 1, 8

The Mean

Mean $= \dfrac{2+3+1+3+1+8}{6}$ ← (total of values) / (number of values)

$= \dfrac{18}{6} = 3$

Mean $= \dfrac{\text{total of values}}{\text{number of values}}$

The Median

1   1   2 | 3   3   8

Median $= \dfrac{2+3}{2} = 2{\cdot}5$

The Median is the middle value once the data set is ordered (smallest to largest) or the mean of the two middle values.

The Mode

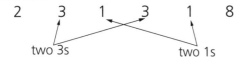

2   3   1   3   1   8

two 3s   two 1s

There are two Modes: 1 and 3.
The Mode is the most frequent value or values.

The Range

2   3   1   3   1   8

least value is 1   greatest value is 8

Range = 8 – 1 = 7
Range = greatest value – least value

Quartiles and the Semi-interquartile Range

Remember the quartiles Q_1, Q_2 and Q_3 split the ordered data set into four equal sets of data:
The Semi-interquartile range is given by:

Q_1 Q_2 Q_3

$\frac{1}{2}(Q_3 - Q_1)$

and gives a measure of the distribution of the data. 'Clumped' data will give a relatively small number and 'spread out' data will give a relatively large number.

Example 9.1

Calculate the Range, Mean, Median and Mode for the data shown in the following frequency table which shows the number of errors made by 30 typists in a typing test.

Number of Errors	0	1	2	3	4	5	6
Frequency	10	7	4	2	4	1	2

Solutions
Add two columns to the frequency table:

No of errors	Frequency	Cumulative Frequency	No of errors × frequency
0	10	10	0 x 10 = 0
1	7	17	1 x 7 = 7
2	4	21	2 x 4 = 8
3	2	23	3 x 2 = 6
4	4	27	4 x 4 = 16
5	1	28	5 x 1 = 5
6	2	30	6 x 2 = 12

Total = 30   Total no. of errors = 54

Greatest no. of errors is 6 and the least is 0.
So Range = 6 – 0 = **6 errors**.

The Mode (most frequent) is **0 errors**.

The Mean $= \dfrac{54}{30}$ ← (Total no. of errors) / (no. of typists)

= **1·8 errors**

The Median (middle value) is the Mean of the 15th and 16th no. of errors when they are listed in increasing order, i.e. $\dfrac{1+1}{2}$ = **1 error**.

Example 9.2

10 girls and 10 boys were chosen at random in a school and given a test consisting of 30 subtractions. The number of errors made was recorded:

Girls: 6, 3, 0, 5, 5, 4, 0, 4, 5, 4
Boys: 9, 3, 2, 10, 6, 5, 2, 1, 7, 2

Calculate the Median and the Semi-Interquartile Range for each of these data sets and comment on the results.

Standard Deviation

Standard Deviation is a measure of the distribution of a data set. It gives a measure of how 'spread out' the values are around their Mean value.

The formula we will use here is:

$$s = \sqrt{\frac{\Sigma(x - \bar{x})^2}{n - 1}}$$

This calculates the Standard Deviation, s, for a sample of values taken from a larger population. Here are the steps required to use this formula:

step 1 Calculate the Mean, $\bar{x}$, of the values:

$$\bar{x} = \frac{\text{sum of values}}{\text{no. of values}} = \frac{\Sigma x}{n}$$

step 2 Calculate the deviation of each value from the Mean:

value − Mean = $x - \bar{x}$.

step 3 Square each deviation:

(value − Mean)2 = $(x - \bar{x})^2$

step 4 Calculate the sum of these squared deviations:

Sum of squared deviations = $\Sigma(x - \bar{x})^2$

(Please turn over.)

Example 9.2 (cont.)

Solution
The ordered data sets are:
Girls: 0 0 3 4 4 | 4 5 5 5 6

$$3 \qquad \frac{4+4}{2} = 4 \qquad 5$$
$$Q_1 \qquad\qquad Q_2 \qquad\qquad Q_3$$

Boys: 1 2 2 2 3 | 5 6 7 9 10

$$2 \qquad \frac{3+5}{2} = 4 \qquad 7$$
$$Q_1 \qquad\qquad Q_2 \qquad\qquad Q_3$$

Semi-interquartile Ranges are:

$$\text{Girls} = \tfrac{1}{2}(Q_3 - Q_1) = \tfrac{1}{2}(5 - 3) = 1$$

$$\text{Boys} = \tfrac{1}{2}(Q_3 - Q_1) = \tfrac{1}{2}(7 - 2) = 2 \cdot 5$$

Although the Median number of errors is the same, 4, for both boys and girls there is much more variation in the number of errors made by boys as indicated by the larger semi-interquartile range for the boys (2·5) compared to that for the girls (1).

Example 9.3

A Quality Control Inspector selects a random sample of six matchboxes produced by a machine and records the number of matches in each:

52 46 50 51 49 52

Calculate the Mean and Standard Deviation for this sample.

Solution:

step 1 Mean $\bar{x} = \frac{52 + 46 + 50 + 51 + 49 + 52}{6} = \frac{300}{6} = 50$

step 2 The deviations from the Mean are:
2, −4, 0, 1, −1, 2

step 3 The squared deviations are:
4, 16, 0, 1, 1, 4

step 4 Sum of the squared deviations:
4 + 16 + 0 + 1 + 1 + 4 = 26

step 5 The Standard Deviation is given by

$$s = \sqrt{\frac{26}{5}} \quad \begin{array}{l}\leftarrow\text{sum of squared deviations} \\ \leftarrow\text{there were 6 values}\end{array}$$

$$= \sqrt{5 \cdot 2} = \mathbf{2 \cdot 3} \text{ (to 1 d.p.)}$$

The Mean number of matches in a box is 50 and the Standard Deviation is 2·3 matches. (Usually around 95% of values are within 2 standard deviations of the Mean. In this case most boxes the machine produces will contain between 45 and 55 matches.)

step 5 Divide the answer in Step 4 by one less than the number of values, then take the square root. This gives the Standard Deviation:

$$s = \sqrt{\frac{\text{sum of squared deviations}}{\text{number of values} - 1}} = \sqrt{\frac{\Sigma(x-\bar{x})^2}{n-1}}$$

(The formula $s = \sqrt{\frac{\Sigma(x-\bar{x})^2}{n-1}}$ used above is one of two formulae given to you in the exam.

The other is: $s = \sqrt{\frac{\Sigma x^2 - (\Sigma x)^2/n}{n-1}}$ and will give the same result.)

Advice
It is best to use a table layout for all the calculations involved in using this formula. The example opposite shows how this may be done.

Note
Scientific and Graphic Calculators have a Statistics or STAT mode. In this mode data sets may be keyed in and various statistics calculated.
For example, after entering the data set:
[n] gives the number of data values;
[Σx] gives the total of the data values;
[$\bar{x}$] gives the mean;
[σ_{n-1}] gives the sample Standard Deviation.
You should consult your calculator manual to find out how to use these facilities.

Example 9.3 (cont.)

In table form:

x Number of matches	$x-\bar{x}$ Deviations from Mean	$(x-\bar{x})^2$ Squared deviations
52	2	4
46	–4	16
50	0	0
51	1	1
49	–1	1
52	2	4

$\Sigma x = 300$ $\qquad$ $\Sigma(x-\bar{x})^2 = 26$

$\bar{x} = \frac{300}{6} = 50$ $\qquad$ $\frac{\Sigma(x-\bar{x})^2}{n-1} = \frac{26}{5} = 5{\cdot}2$

so s (Standard Deviation) = $\sqrt{5{\cdot}2}$ = **2·3** (to 1 d. p.)

Scatter Graphs and Lines of Best Fit

If you are good at maths are you likely to be musical?

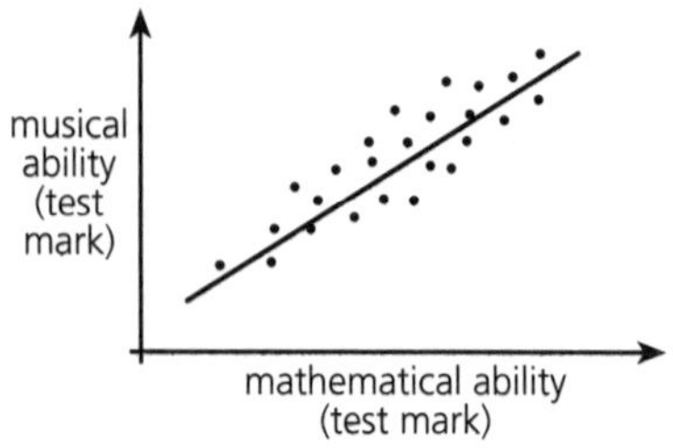

For this sample of students the answer is yes. There is a positive correlation between these abilities.

Do you make fewer errors the longer you practice?

For this sample of typists the answer is yes. There is a negative correlation between number of errors and number of hours of practice.

Do heavy people read more or less books than light people?

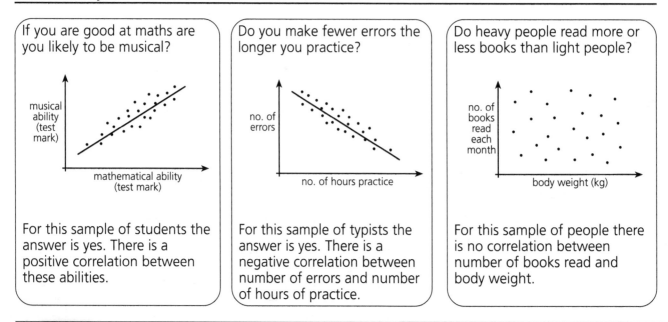

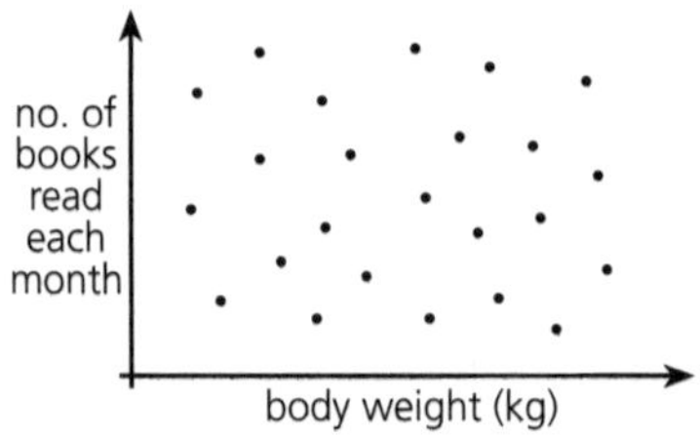

For this sample of people there is no correlation between number of books read and body weight.

Example 9.4

A sample of six fathers and their grown-up sons were weighed. The results are given in the table:

Father's weight (kg)	62	67	70	71	68	64
Son's weight (kg)	63	66	67	68	66	63

(a) Draw a scattergraph for this data and describe the type of correlation involved.
(b) Draw a 'line of best fit', find its equation and use this to predict the weight of a man whose father weighed 75 kg.

Solution

(a)

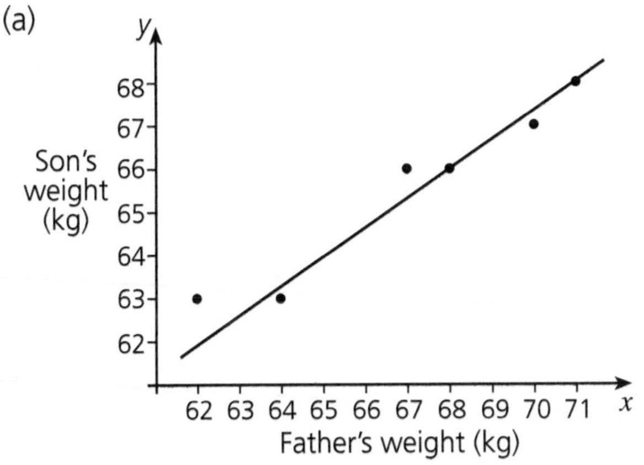

There is a positive correlation between the father's weight and the son's weight.

(b) The equation of the best-fitting line is

$$y = mx + c$$

gradient (m) — y-intercept (c)

To calculate the gradient pick two suitable points at either end of the line:

(62, 62) and (71, 68)

$$m = \frac{68 - 62}{71 - 62} \quad \leftarrow y\text{-difference},\ \leftarrow x\text{-difference}$$

$$= \frac{6}{9} = \frac{2}{3} = 0{\cdot}66\ldots$$

so $y = 0{\cdot}66\ldots \times x + c$. Now use one of the points on the line, e.g. (71, 68)

so $68 = 0{\cdot}66\ldots \times 71 + c$

giving $c = 68 - 0{\cdot}66\ldots \times 71 = 20{\cdot}66\ldots$

The equation is

$y \doteqdot 0{\cdot}67x + 20{\cdot}67$ (to 2 d. p.)

When $x = 75$

$y \doteqdot 0{\cdot}67 \times 75 + 20{\cdot}67 \doteqdot 71$ kg (to the nearest kg)

Probability

The probability of an event happening is a number from 0 to 1:

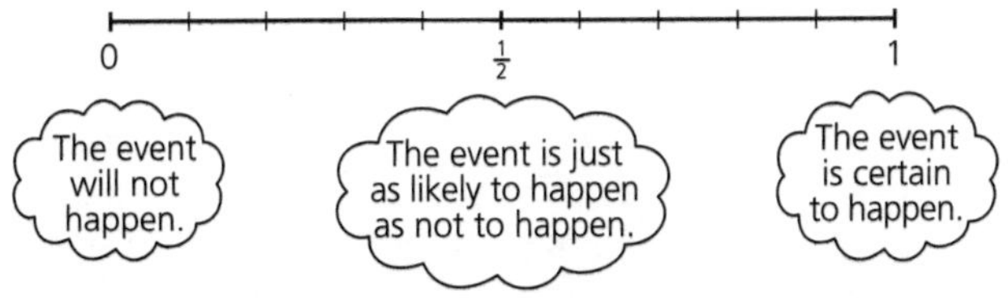

In some cases your knowledge of a situation will allow you to calculate the probability of an event happening:

$$\text{Probability of an event} = \frac{\text{no. of outcomes that make the event happen}}{\text{total no. of possible outcomes in the situation}}$$

Example 9.5

Which is more likely: drawing a face card from a pack of cards or rolling a six with a dice?

Solution

Each of the 4 suits has 3 face cards (J, Q and K) so there are 12 face cards out of 52 cards:

Probability of drawing a face card $= \frac{12}{52} \doteqdot 0{\cdot}23$ (to 2 d. p.)

Rolling a six can happen in 1 way out of 6 possible outcomes:

Probability of rolling a six $= \frac{1}{6} \doteqdot 0{\cdot}17$ (to 2 d. p.)

Drawing a face card has a higher probability and so is more likely.

For example if the event is: 'rolling an odd prime with a dice' then two outcomes 3 and 5 allow the event to happen. In this situation there are 6 possible outcomes (rolling 1 up to 6).

Probability of rolling an odd prime

$= \text{P(odd prime)} = \frac{2}{6}$ ← favourable outcomes (numerator 2) / possible outcomes (denominator 6)

$= \frac{1}{3}$

Note 1

If p is the probability of an event happening then (1 – p) is the probability of the event **not** happening. In the example of rolling an odd prime $1 - \frac{1}{3} = \frac{2}{3}$ is the probability of not rolling an odd prime.

Note 2

Probabilities can also be estimated from a sample data set as in the example opposite.

Example 9.6

A random sample of 50 school students were asked the number of children in their families (including themselves). The results were:

No. of children in family	1	2	3	4	5	6
No. of students	8	24	16	1	0	1

Estimate the probability of a randomly picked student having only 1 brother or sister. How many such students would you expect at the school if the total roll is 1000 students?

Solution

P(family size 2) $= \frac{24}{50} = 0{\cdot}48$

Expected no. at school $= 0{\cdot}48 \times 1000$

$= \mathbf{480}$

Cancelling Fractions

With Numbers

$\frac{10}{2} = \frac{{}^1\cancel{2} \times 5}{{}^1\cancel{2}} = \frac{5}{1} = 5$

$\frac{10}{14} = \frac{{}^1\cancel{2} \times 5}{{}^1\cancel{2} \times 7} = \frac{5}{7}$

$\frac{7^2}{3 \times 7} = \frac{7 \times {}^1\cancel{7}}{3 \times {}^1\cancel{7}} = \frac{7}{3}$

With Letters

$\frac{x(x+3)}{x} = \frac{{}^1\cancel{x} \times (x+3)}{{}^1\cancel{x}} = \frac{x+3}{1} = x+3$

$\frac{(x-1)(x+2)}{(x-1)(x+5)} = \frac{{}^1\cancel{(x-1)} \times (x+2)}{{}^1\cancel{(x-1)} \times (x+5)} = \frac{x+2}{x+5}$

$\frac{(2x+1)^2}{3(2x+1)} = \frac{(2x+1) \times {}^1\cancel{(2x+1)}}{3 \times {}^1\cancel{(2x+1)}} = \frac{2x+1}{3}$

Note

$\frac{a+b}{a}$ No cancelling allowed.

$\frac{a \times b}{a}$ Cancelling is allowed: $\frac{{}^1\cancel{a} \times b}{{}^1\cancel{a}} = \frac{b}{1} = b$

With Numbers

$\frac{45}{50}$ — 45: Factorise; 50: Factorise

$= \frac{{}^1\cancel{5} \times 9}{{}^1\cancel{5} \times 10}$ Cancel the factor 5

$= \frac{9}{10}$

With Letters

$\frac{x^2 - y^2}{10x - 10y}$ — $x^2 - y^2$: factorise (difference of squares); $10x - 10y$: factorise (common factors)

$= \frac{{}^1\cancel{(x-y)}(x+y)}{10{}^1\cancel{(x-y)}}$ cancel the factor $(x - y)$

$= \frac{x+y}{10}$

Multiplying Fractions

The basic rule is:

$\frac{a}{b} \times \frac{c}{d} = \frac{ac}{bd}$

The two numerators are multiplied.

The two denominators are multiplied.

Cancelling of any factor found in both numerator and denominator can then take place.
It is often easier to do this cancelling before doing the multiplication:

With Numbers

$\frac{7}{15} \times \frac{12}{49}$

$= \frac{{}^1\cancel{7}}{{}^5\cancel{15}} \times \frac{{}^4\cancel{12}}{{}^7\cancel{49}}$

$= \frac{1 \times 4}{5 \times 7} = \frac{4}{35}$

With Letters

$\frac{x}{6} \times \frac{3(x+1)}{x^2}$

$= \frac{{}^1\cancel{x}}{{}^2\cancel{6}} \times \frac{{}^1\cancel{3}(x+1)}{x \times {}^1\cancel{x}}$

$= \frac{1 \times (x+1)}{2 \times x} = \frac{(x+1)}{2x}$

Example 10.1

Simplify:

(a) $\frac{(2x-1)^2}{(2x-1)^3}$ (b) $\frac{3(x-1)(x+1)}{6(x+1)^2}$

Solution

(a) $\frac{(2x-1)^2}{(2x-1)^3} = \frac{{}^1\cancel{(2x-1)}{}^1\cancel{(2x-1)}}{(2x-1){}^1\cancel{(2x-1)}{}^1\cancel{(2x-1)}} = \mathbf{\frac{1}{(2x-1)}}$

(b) $\frac{3(x-1)(x+1)}{6(x+1)^2} = \frac{{}^1\cancel{3}(x-1){}^1\cancel{(x+1)}}{{}^2\cancel{6}(x+1){}^1\cancel{(x+1)}} = \mathbf{\frac{(x-1)}{2(x+1)}}$

Example 10.2

Simplify:

(a) $\frac{2a^2 - 8b^2}{4a + 8b}$ (b) $\frac{x^2 - 7x + 12}{x^2 - 16}$

Solution

(a) $\frac{2a^2 - 8b^2}{4a + 8b} = \frac{2(a^2 - 4b^2)}{4(a + 2b)}$ ← Not fully factorised

$= \frac{{}^1\cancel{2}(a-2b){}^1\cancel{(a+2b)}}{{}^2\cancel{4}{}^1\cancel{(a+2b)}}$ Cancel factors 2 and $(a + 2b)$

$= \mathbf{\frac{a-2b}{2}}$

(b) $\frac{x^2 - 7x + 12}{x^2 - 16} = \frac{{}^1\cancel{(x-4)}(x-3)}{{}^1\cancel{(x-4)}(x+4)}$

$= \mathbf{\frac{(x-3)}{(x+4)}}$

Example 10.3

Simplify:

(a) $\frac{2x}{3} \times \frac{6y}{xy}$ (b) $\frac{3(x+1)^2}{5} \times \frac{1}{6(x+1)}$

Solution

(a) $\frac{2\cancel{x}}{{}^1\cancel{3}} \times \frac{{}^2\cancel{6}\cancel{y}}{{}^1\cancel{x}\cancel{y}}$ The cancelled factors are 3, x and y.

$= \frac{2 \times 2}{1 \times 1} = \frac{4}{1} = \mathbf{4}$

(b) $\frac{{}^1\cancel{3}(x+1){}^1\cancel{(x+1)}}{5} \times \frac{1}{{}^2\cancel{6}{}^1\cancel{(x+1)}}$ The cancelled factors are 3 and $(x + 1)$.

$= \frac{(x+1) \times 1}{5 \times 2} = \mathbf{\frac{x+1}{10}}$

Dividing Fractions

Each division, for example $\frac{2a}{b} \div \frac{a^2}{b}$, can be written as a 'double-decker' fraction:

$$\frac{\frac{2a}{b}}{\frac{a^2}{b}}$$

The top and bottom of a fraction may be multiplied by the same number (or letter). In this case multiply top and bottom by b.

$$= \frac{\frac{2a}{b} \times b}{\frac{a^2}{b} \times b} = \frac{2a}{a^2} = \frac{2a}{a \times a} = \frac{2}{a}$$

This method copes with, for example, $\frac{3x}{4} \div 2$:

$$\frac{\frac{3x}{4}}{2}$$

Multiply top and bottom by 4 to get rid of the 4 in $\frac{3x}{4}$.

$$= \frac{\frac{3x}{4} \times 4}{2 \times 4} = \frac{3x}{8}$$

and also examples such as $8 \div \frac{a^2}{6}$:

$$\frac{8}{\frac{a^2}{6}}$$

Multiply top and bottom by 6 to get rid of the 6 in $\frac{a^2}{6}$.

$$= \frac{8 \times 6}{\frac{a^2}{6} \times 6} = \frac{48}{a^2}$$

Example 10.4

Express each of these as a single fraction in its simplest form:

(a) $\frac{3a}{7(a+1)} \div \frac{6}{(a+1)^2}$ (b) $2x \div \frac{2}{3x}$

Solution

(a) $$\frac{\frac{3a}{7(a+1)} \times 7(a+1)(a+1)}{\frac{6}{(a+1)(a+1)} \times 7(a+1)(a+1)}$$

$$= \frac{3a(a+1)}{42} = \mathbf{\frac{a(a+1)}{14}}$$

(b) $$\frac{2x \times 3x}{\frac{2}{3x} \times 3x}$$

$$= \frac{6x^2}{2} = \frac{3x^2}{1} = \mathbf{3x^2}$$

Adding and Subtracting Fractions

Aim to get the two denominators equal:

With Numbers

$\frac{2}{3} + \frac{1}{5}$

$= \frac{2 \times 5}{3 \times 5} + \frac{1 \times 3}{5 \times 3}$

$= \frac{10}{15} + \frac{3}{15}$ both '15th's

$= \frac{10+3}{15} = \frac{13}{15}$

With Letters

$\frac{2}{a} + \frac{1}{b}$

$= \frac{2 \times b}{a \times b} + \frac{1 \times a}{b \times a}$

$= \frac{2b}{ab} + \frac{a}{ab}$ both 'abth's

$= \frac{2b+a}{ab}$

Example 10.5

Express $\frac{2}{x^2} + \frac{1}{2x}$ as a single fraction.

Solution

$\frac{2}{x^2} + \frac{1}{2x}$ Aim: change both denominators to $2x^2$

$= \frac{2 \times 2}{x^2 \times 2} + \frac{1 \times x}{2x \times x}$

$= \frac{4}{2x^2} + \frac{x}{2x^2} = \mathbf{\frac{4+x}{2x^2}}$

Note 1

When making the two denominators the same look closely at the factors of each denominator:

for a and $3a^2$ make both $3a^2$

$(3 \times a \times a)$ $(3 \times a \times a)$

missing factor 3 and factor a so multiply by $3a$

for $2ab^2$ and $3a^2b$ change to $6a^2b^2$

$(2 \times a \times b \times b)$ $(3 \times a \times a \times b)$ $(2 \times 3 \times a \times a \times b \times b)$

missing factors 3 and a so multiply by $3a$

missing factors 2 and b so multiply by $2b$

Note 2

Always check your answer to see if cancelling is possible.

$$\frac{a+4}{3a} - \frac{1-2a}{3a} = \frac{a+4-(1-2a)}{3a}$$

$$= \frac{a+4-1+2a}{3a} = \frac{3a+3}{3a} \quad \text{Common factor of 3}$$

$$= \frac{3(a+1)}{3a} = \frac{a+1}{a}$$

Changing the Subject of a Formula

At all times the aim is to isolate the required letter by treating both sides of the formula identically.

For example:

$v = \sqrt{9-u^2}$

square | square

$v^2 = 9 - u^2$

add u^2 | add u^2

$v^2 + u^2 = 9$

subtract v^2 | subtract v^2

$u^2 = 9 - v^2$

square root | square root

$\mathbf{u} = \sqrt{\mathbf{9 - v^2}}$

To change the subject to $\boldsymbol{u}$ get rid of the square root by doing the 'opposite', namely squaring.

It is easier without a minus sign in front of u^2 so do the 'opposite', namely add $\boldsymbol{u}^2$.

Get rid of v^2 by subtracting it from both sides.

Finally get rid of squaring by doing the 'opposite', namely, square rooting.

$\boldsymbol{u}$ is now the subject of the formula

Example 10.6

Express as a single fraction in its simplest form:

$$\frac{5}{x} - \frac{2}{x-3}$$

Solution

$$\frac{5}{x} - \frac{2}{x-3}$$

Change both denominators to $x(x-3)$

$$= \frac{5 \times (x-3)}{x \times (x-3)} - \frac{2 \times x}{(x-3) \times x}$$

$$= \frac{5(x-3)}{x(x-3)} - \frac{2x}{x(x-3)}$$

$$= \frac{5(x-3) - 2x}{x(x-3)}$$

Now start to simplify.

$$= \frac{5x - 15 - 2x}{x(x-3)}$$

$$= \frac{3x-15}{x(x-3)}$$

$$= \frac{3(x-5)}{x(x-3)}$$

(No cancelling possible!)

Example 10.7

Change the subject in the formulae:

(a) $r = \sqrt{\frac{A}{\pi}}$ to A (b) $s = \frac{(u+v)t}{2}$ to t

Solution

(a) $r = \sqrt{\frac{A}{\pi}}$

square | square

$r^2 = \frac{A}{\pi}$

$\times \pi$ | $\times \pi$

$\pi r^2 = A$

so $\mathbf{A} = \boldsymbol{\pi r^2}$ (Is this familiar?)

(b) $s = \frac{(u+v)t}{2}$

$\times 2$ | $\times 2$

$2s = (u+v)t$

divide by $u + v$ | divide by $u + v$

$\frac{2s}{u+v} = t$

so $\boldsymbol{t} = \boldsymbol{\frac{2s}{u+v}}$

10. Further Algebraic Operations

Notes

In achieving your aim of isolating the required letter identify what you want rid of and do the opposite to each side.

For example:

You want rid of	Do this to both sides
+2	subtract 2
$\frac{\text{(something)}}{5}$	multiply by 5
$\sqrt{\text{something}}$	square
$(\text{something})^2$	square root

Simplifying Surds

For our purposes a surd is a square root of a number that on your calculator would give you an 'endless' decimal:

$\sqrt{2}$

$\sqrt{25}$

When you are asked to 'simplify' a surd you have to make the number under the root sign as small as possible. How is this done?

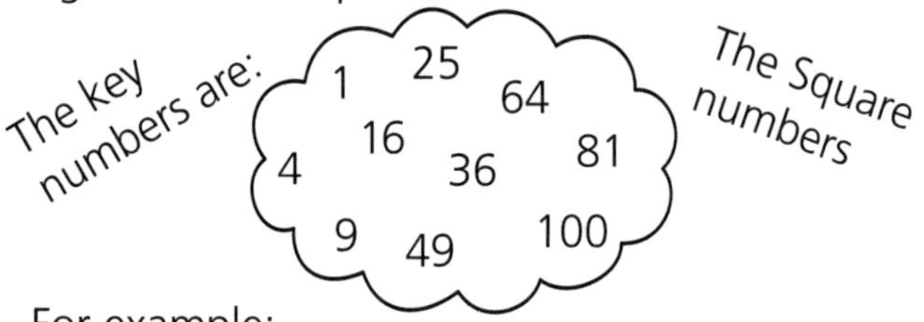

For example:

$$\sqrt{108} = \sqrt{9 \times 12} = \sqrt{9} \times \sqrt{12} = 3 \times \sqrt{12}$$

However $\sqrt{12}$ can still be simplified:

$$3 \times \sqrt{12} = 3 \times \sqrt{4 \times 3} = 3 \times \sqrt{4} \times \sqrt{3}$$
$$= 3 \times 2 \times \sqrt{3} = 6 \times \sqrt{3}$$

Write this as $6\sqrt{3}$. (Compare with $6 \times x$ written as $6x$.)

Alternatively:

$$\sqrt{108} = \sqrt{36 \times 3} = \sqrt{36} \times \sqrt{3} = 6 \times \sqrt{3} = 6\sqrt{3}$$

General rules are:

$$\sqrt{a \times b} = \sqrt{a} \times \sqrt{b}$$

and

$$\sqrt{\frac{a}{b}} = \frac{\sqrt{a}}{\sqrt{b}}$$

Example 10.8

Simplify:

(a) $\sqrt{96}$ (b) $\sqrt{2} \times \sqrt{8}$

(c) $\frac{\sqrt{6}}{\sqrt{2}}$ (d) $\sqrt{\frac{49}{100}}$

Solution

(a) $\sqrt{96} = \sqrt{16 \times 6} = \sqrt{16} \times \sqrt{6}$
$= 4 \times \sqrt{6} = \mathbf{4\sqrt{6}}$

(b) $\sqrt{2} \times \sqrt{8} = \sqrt{2 \times 8} = \sqrt{16} = \mathbf{4}$
(or $\sqrt{2} \times \sqrt{8} = \sqrt{2} \times \sqrt{2} \times \sqrt{4} = 2 \times 2 = \mathbf{4}$)

(c) $\frac{\sqrt{6}}{\sqrt{2}} = \sqrt{\frac{6}{2}} = \mathbf{\sqrt{3}}$

(or $\frac{\sqrt{6}}{\sqrt{2}} = \frac{\sqrt{2} \times \sqrt{3}}{\sqrt{2}} = \mathbf{\sqrt{3}}$)

(d) $\sqrt{\frac{49}{100}} = \frac{\sqrt{49}}{\sqrt{100}} = \frac{7}{10} = \mathbf{0{\cdot}7}$

Rationalising the Denominator

1. $\sqrt{a} \times \sqrt{a} = a$

You can use this fact to get rid of root signs on the denominators of fractions.
For example:

$$\frac{2}{\sqrt{3}} = \frac{2 \times \sqrt{3}}{\sqrt{3} \times \sqrt{3}} = \frac{2\sqrt{3}}{3}$$ ← no root sign

In general:

$$\frac{a}{\sqrt{b}} = \frac{a \times \sqrt{b}}{\sqrt{b} \times \sqrt{b}} = \frac{a\sqrt{b}}{b}$$ ← no root sign

2. $(a - \sqrt{b})(a + \sqrt{b})$
$= a^2 + a\sqrt{b} - a\sqrt{b} - b = a^2 - b$

You can use this fact to get rid of root signs in the denominators of fractions like this:

$$\frac{2}{4 - \sqrt{3}} = \frac{2 \times (4 + \sqrt{3})}{(4 - \sqrt{3}) \times (4 + \sqrt{3})}$$

$$= \frac{2(4 + \sqrt{3})}{16 + 4\sqrt{3} - 4\sqrt{3} - 3} = \frac{8 + 2\sqrt{3}}{13}$$ ← no root sign

Example 10.9

Express as a fraction with a rational denominator:

(a) $\frac{3}{\sqrt{6}}$ (b) $\frac{2}{\sqrt{18}}$ (c) $\frac{3}{5 + \sqrt{7}}$

Solution

(a) $$\frac{3}{\sqrt{6}} = \frac{3 \times \sqrt{6}}{\sqrt{6} \times \sqrt{6}} = \frac{{}^{1}\cancel{3}\sqrt{6}}{{}_{2}\cancel{6}} = \mathbf{\frac{\sqrt{6}}{2}}$$

(b) $$\frac{2}{\sqrt{18}} = \frac{2}{\sqrt{9 \times 2}} = \frac{2}{\sqrt{9} \times \sqrt{2}} = \frac{2}{3\sqrt{2}}$$

$$= \frac{2 \times \sqrt{2}}{3\sqrt{2} \times \sqrt{2}} = \frac{{}^{1}\cancel{2}\sqrt{2}}{{}_{3}\cancel{6}} = \mathbf{\frac{\sqrt{2}}{3}}$$

(c) $$\frac{3}{5 + \sqrt{7}} = \frac{3 \times (5 - \sqrt{7})}{(5 + \sqrt{7}) \times (5 - \sqrt{7})}$$

$$= \frac{3(5 - \sqrt{7})}{25 - 5\sqrt{7} + 5\sqrt{7} - 7} = \frac{{}^{1}\cancel{3}(5 - \sqrt{7})}{{}_{6}\cancel{18}}$$

$$= \mathbf{\frac{5 - \sqrt{7}}{6}}$$

Working with Indices

Rule	Comments	Examples
$x^m \times x^n = x^{m+n}$	When multiplying, the indices are added. Note: not in the case $x^m \times y^n$!	$a^2 \times a^3 = a^{2+3} = a^5$
$\frac{x^m}{x^n} = x^{m-n}$	When dividing, the indices are subtracted.	$\frac{c^7}{c^3} = c^{7-3} = c^4$
$(x^m)^n = x^{mn}$	When raising a power to a power, multiply the indices.	$(y^3)^4 = y^{3 \times 4} = y^{12}$
$x^0 = 1$	Any number or expression (other than zero) raised to the power zero gives 1.	$2^0 = 1$ $(\frac{1}{2})^0 = 1$ $(a + b)^0 = 1$
$x^{-n} = \frac{1}{x^n}$	Something to a negative power can be rewritten as 1 divided by the same thing to the positive power.	$a^{-1} = \frac{1}{a^1} = \frac{1}{a}$ $a^{-3} = \frac{1}{a^3}$
$x^{\frac{m}{n}} = (\sqrt[n]{x})^m$	For a fractional power, the top number gives the power, and the bottom number gives the type of root. (2 means square root, 3 means cube root, etc...)	$a^{\frac{3}{2}}$ (3 ← power 3, 2 ← square root) $= (\sqrt{a})^3$ $a^{\frac{2}{3}}$ (2 ← power 2, 3 ← cube root) $= (\sqrt[3]{a})^2$

Example 10.10

Simplify: (a) $\frac{y^3y^5}{y^2}$ (b) $5x^{-2} \times 2x$ (c) $a^{\frac{1}{2}} \times 4a^{-\frac{3}{2}}$ (d) $6a^2 \div 3a$

(e) $(m^{-\frac{3}{2}})^4$ Write your answer using positive indices where possible.

Solution (a) $\frac{y^3y^5}{y^2}$ ← add these indices and subtract this index

$= y^{3+5-2} = y^6$

(b) $5x^{-2} \times 2x$
$= 5x^{-2} \times 2x^1$
$= 10x^{-2+1}$
$= 10x^{-1} = \frac{10}{x}$

(c) $a^{\frac{1}{2}} \times 4a^{-\frac{3}{2}}$
$= 4a^{\frac{1}{2}+(-\frac{3}{2})}$
$= 4a^{-1}$
$= \frac{4}{a}$

(d) $6a^2 \div 3a = \frac{{}^2\cancel{6}a^2}{{}^1\cancel{3}a^1}$
$= 2a^{2-1} = 2a^1 = 2a$

(e) $(m^{-\frac{3}{2}})^4 = m^{-\frac{3}{2}\times 4}$
$= m^{-6} = \frac{1}{m^6}$

Example 10.11

Change to index form ax^n: $\frac{1}{\sqrt{2x^3}}$

Solution $\frac{1}{\sqrt{2x^3}} = \frac{1}{\sqrt{2}\sqrt{x^3}} = \frac{1}{\sqrt{2}} \times \frac{1}{x^{\frac{3}{2}}} = \frac{1}{\sqrt{2}}x^{-\frac{3}{2}}$

11. Quadratic Graphs and Equations

The Parabola

A graph showing the values of x^2 for all values of x can be built up from a few particular values:

x	−3	−2	−1	0	1	2	3
$y = x^2$	9	4	1	0	1	4	9

(−3, 9) (−2, 4) (−1, 1) (0, 0) (1, 1) (2, 4) (3, 9)

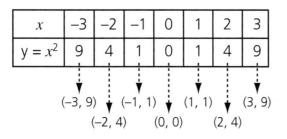

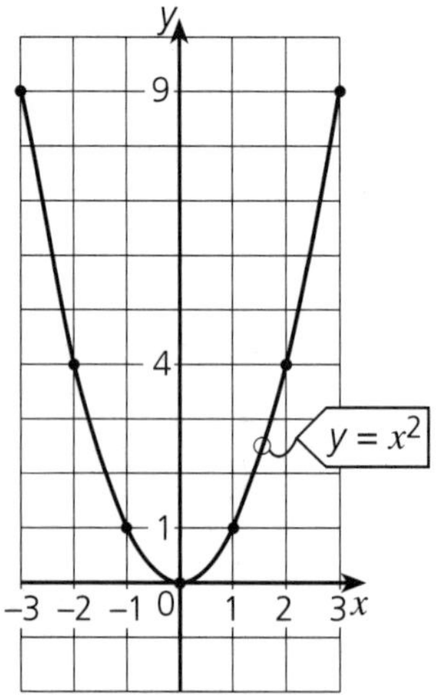

Notes

(1) This type of graph shape is called a **Parabola**.
(2) The graph is symmetric, with the y-axis (the line $x = 0$) being the axis of symmetry.
(3) The graph has a minimum turning point at the origin (0, 0). This means that x^2 has a minimum value of 0 when $x = 0$.
(4) The equation $y = 0$ or $x^2 = 0$ has one **Solution** (**Root**), namely $x = 0$.

Quadratic Graphs

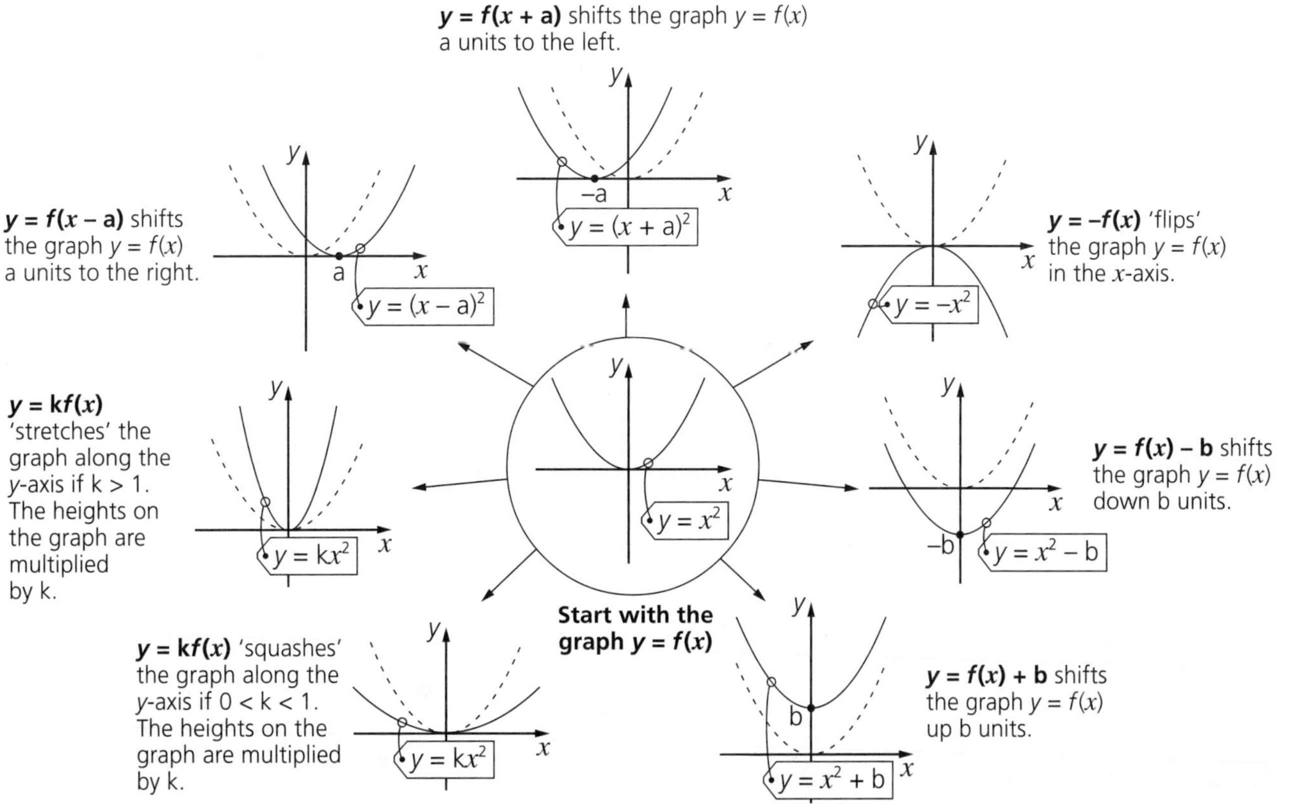

$y = f(x + a)$ shifts the graph $y = f(x)$ a units to the left.
–a
$y = (x + a)^2$
$y = f(x - a)$ shifts the graph $y = f(x)$ a units to the right.
a
$y = (x - a)^2$
$y = -f(x)$ 'flips' the graph $y = f(x)$ in the x-axis.
$y = -x^2$
$y = kf(x)$ 'stretches' the graph along the y-axis if $k > 1$. The heights on the graph are multiplied by k.
$y = kx^2$
$y = x^2$
Start with the graph $y = f(x)$
$y = f(x) - b$ shifts the graph $y = f(x)$ down b units.
–b
$y = x^2 - b$
$y = kf(x)$ 'squashes' the graph along the y-axis if $0 < k < 1$. The heights on the graph are multiplied by k.
$y = kx^2$
$y = f(x) + b$ shifts the graph $y = f(x)$ up b units.
b
$y = x^2 + b$

A quadratic graph has an equation of the form: $y = ax^2 + bx + c$ (where $a \neq 0$)

- There must be an 'x^2 term' which can be positive or negative.
- There may or may not be an 'x term'.
- There may or may not be a 'constant term'.

The shape of this type of graph is always a parabola:

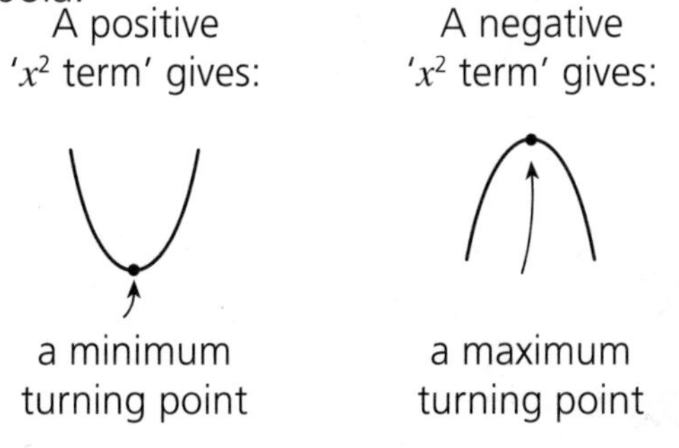

A positive 'x^2 term' gives:
A negative 'x^2 term' gives:

The equation can also be written in the form:

$$y = k(x + a)^2 + b$$

- k: Scales the parabola along the y-axis
- a: Moves the graph $y = x^2$ left or right as a is positive or negative
- b: Moves the graph up or down as b is positive or negative

Example 11.1

The diagram shows the graph of $y = kx^2$. Use the information in the diagram to calculate the value of k.

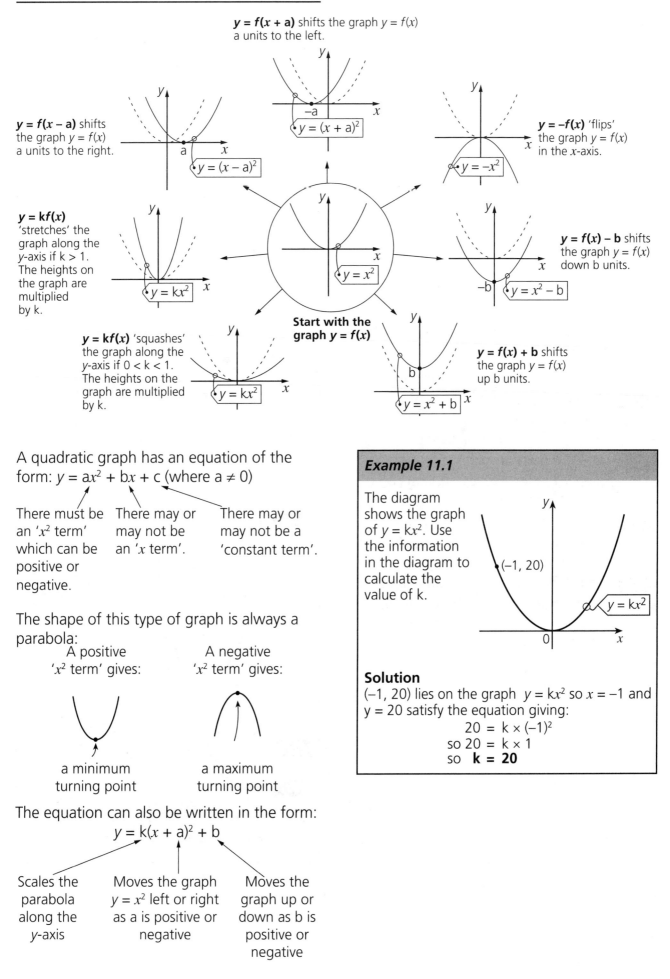

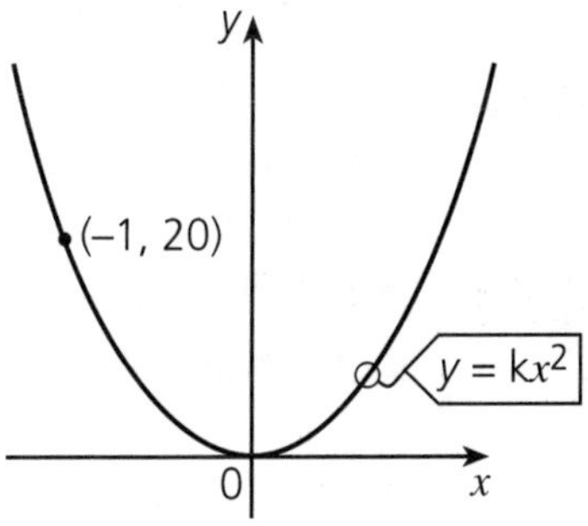

Solution

$(-1, 20)$ lies on the graph $y = kx^2$ so $x = -1$ and $y = 20$ satisfy the equation giving:

$$20 = k \times (-1)^2$$
$$\text{so } 20 = k \times 1$$
$$\text{so } \mathbf{k = 20}$$

11. Quadratic Graphs and Equations

To find maximum or minimum turning points, make the squared term $(x + a)^2$ equal to zero. This will happen when $x = -a$

$y = (x + a)^2 + b$ → $y = 0^2 + b = b$

The minimum turning point is (–a, b).

$y = b - (x + a)^2$ → $y = b - 0^2 = b$

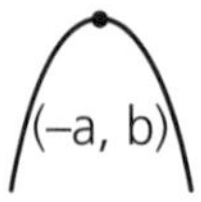

The maximum turning point is (–a, b).

In both cases the axis of symmetry is $x = -a$.

Example 11.2

(a) Determine the minimum turning point on the graph $y = (x - 2)^2 - 4$

(b) Determine the maximum turning point on the graph $y = 7 - (x + 3)^2$

Solution

(a) $y = (x - 2)^2 - 4$

Make this zero, so $x - 2 = 0$ giving $x = 2$
and $y = 0^2 - 4 = -4$

The minimum turning point is **(2, –4)**

(b) $y = 7 - (x + 3)^2$

Make this zero, so $x + 3 = 0$ giving $x = -3$
and $y = 7 - 0^2 = 7$

The maximum turning point is **(–3, 7)**

Quadratic Equations: Solutions by Graphs

To solve $ax^2 + bx + c = 0$ using a graph:

step 1 Construct a table of values of y for various values of x where
$$y = ax^2 + bx + c$$

step 2 Use the pairs of values (x, y) from step 1 to plot a series of points on a suitably scaled x-y axis diagram.

step 3 The solutions to $ax^2 + bx + c = 0$ are the values of x where the graph crosses the x-axis.

step 4 Check the solutions by substituting each value into $ax^2 + bx + c$. If your solution is correct it will give you a value of zero.

Example 11.3

Solve $4x^2 - 8x - 5 = 0$ by drawing a suitable graph.

Solution

step 1 The table of values is:

x	–3	–2	–1	0	1	2	3
$y = 4x^2 - 8x - 5$	55	27	7	–5	–9	–5	7

step 2 The graph is:

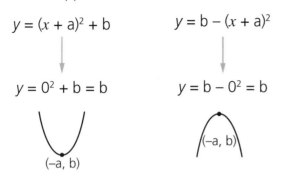

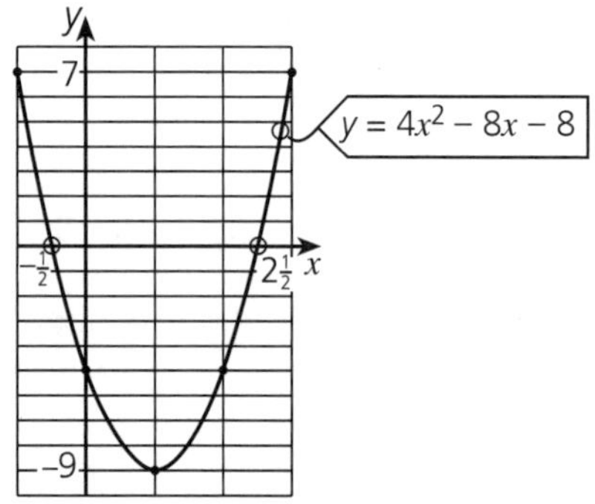

step 3 $x = -\frac{1}{2}$ or $x = 2\frac{1}{2}$

step 4 Check:

$4 \times (-\frac{1}{2})^2 - 8 \times (-\frac{1}{2}) - 5 = 0$ ✓

$4 \times (2\frac{1}{2})^2 - 8 \times (2\frac{1}{2}) - 5 = 0$ ✓

Quadratic Equations: Solutions by Factorising

The general method is as follows:

quadratic expression = 0

↓

(1st factor) × (2nd factor) = 0 ★

↙ ↘

1st factor = 0 or 2nd factor = 0

↓ ↓

Solve to get 1st solution | Solve to get 2nd solution

Note

At step ★ you use the fact that if you multiply two numbers to get zero then one or other of the two numbers is zero:

a × b = 0

↙ ↘

a = 0 or b = 0

Example 11.4

Solve $x^2 - 2x - 3 = 0$

Solution

$$x^2 - 2x - 3 = 0$$
$$(x + 1)(x - 3) = 0$$

$x + 1 = 0$ or $x - 3 = 0$

$x = -1$ $\quad x = 3$

The two roots of the equation are –1 and 3.

Example 11.5

Find the roots of the following quadratic equations:
(a) $3x^2 + 5x - 2 = 0$ (b) $3x^2 + 5x = 0$

Solution

(a) $3x^2 + 5x - 2 = 0$

$(3x - 1)(x + 2) = 0$

$3x - 1 = 0$ or $x + 2 = 0$

$3x = 1$ $\quad x = -2$

$x = \frac{1}{3}$

The roots are $\frac{1}{3}$ and –2.

(b) $3x^2 + 5x = 0$

$x(3x + 5) = 0$

$x = 0$ or $3x + 5 = 0$

$3x = -5$

$x = -\frac{5}{3}$

The roots are 0 and $-\frac{5}{3}$.

Quadratic Equations: Solutions by Formula

When solving $ax^2 + bx + c = 0$, sometimes (?)(?) = 0 (the factorising step) does not work, i.e. the expression does not factorise.
In this case you use the Quadratic Formula:

$$ax^2 + bx + c = 0$$

$$x = \frac{-b + \sqrt{b^2 - 4ac}}{2a} \text{ or } x = \frac{-b - \sqrt{b^2 - 4ac}}{2a}$$

These are the two roots or solutions of the equation.

The compact way of writing this is $x = \frac{-b \pm \sqrt{b^2 - 4ac}}{2a}$

± means there are two possibilities: one from adding, the other from subtracting.

Example 11.6

Solve $3x^2 - 4x - 2 = 0$ using an appropriate formula giving your answer correct to 1 decimal place.

Solution

$$3x^2 - 4x - 2 = 0$$

compare $ax^2 + bx + c = 0$

This gives a = 3 (the number of 'x^2's)

b = –4 (the number of 'x's)

and c = –2 (the constant term)

The appropriate formula is $x = \dfrac{-b \pm \sqrt{b^2 - 4ac}}{2a}$

which becomes: $x = \dfrac{-(-4) \pm \sqrt{(-4)^2 - 4 \times 3 \times (-2)}}{2 \times 3} = \dfrac{4 \pm \sqrt{16 + 24}}{6}$

$$= \frac{4 \pm \sqrt{40}}{6}$$

so $x = \dfrac{4 + \sqrt{40}}{6} \doteqdot 1{\cdot}7$ or $x = \dfrac{4 - \sqrt{40}}{6} \doteqdot -0{\cdot}4$

(to 1 d. p.) (to 1 d. p.)

Note on Graphic Calculators

Graphic Calculators are great for checking results. Usually a mistake in your calculation can be detected from a quick graph.

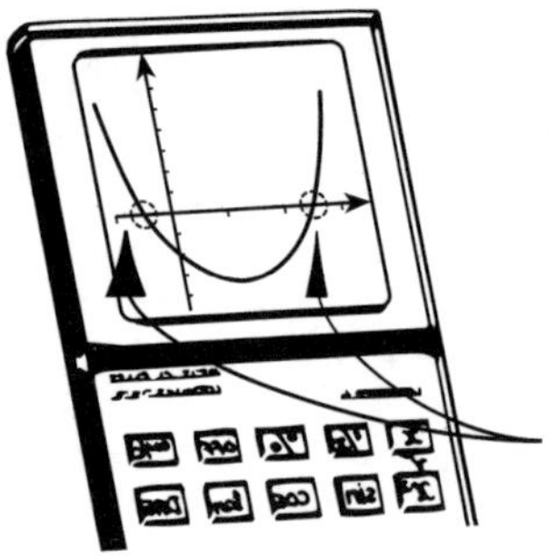

Graph: $y = 3x^2 - 4x - 2$
with Xmin: –1 Ymin: –5
max: 2 max: 5
scl: 1 scl: 1

These intersections seem reasonable for $x \doteqdot -0{\cdot}4$ and $x \doteqdot 1{\cdot}7$. You could 'zoom in' to check the results of your calculation more accurately.

Warning

Results written down directly from your Graphic Calculator will gain no marks. Full working is required. A Graphic Calculator is only useful for detecting possible errors in your calculation of the solution of an equation.

The Sine, Cosine and Tangent Graphs

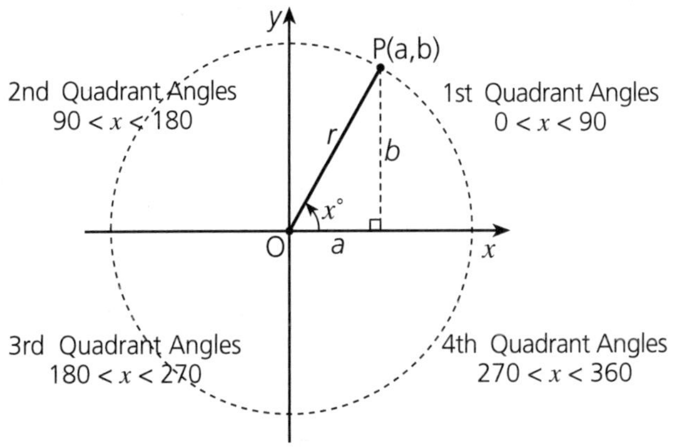

From a starting position along the x-axis, line OP rotates about the origin O anticlockwise x° as shown in the diagram.
Here are three definitions:

$\sin x^{\circ} = \dfrac{b}{r}$ $\quad\cos x^{\circ} = \dfrac{a}{r}$ $\quad\tan x^{\circ} = \dfrac{b}{a}$

Since a and b are coordinates they may be positive or negative.
r is the length of OP so is always positive.

You can draw graphs showing the values of these three TRIGONOMETRIC FUNCTIONS $\sin x^{\circ}$, $\cos x^{\circ}$ and $\tan x^{\circ}$ as OP rotates from 0° through all 4 quadrants to 360°:

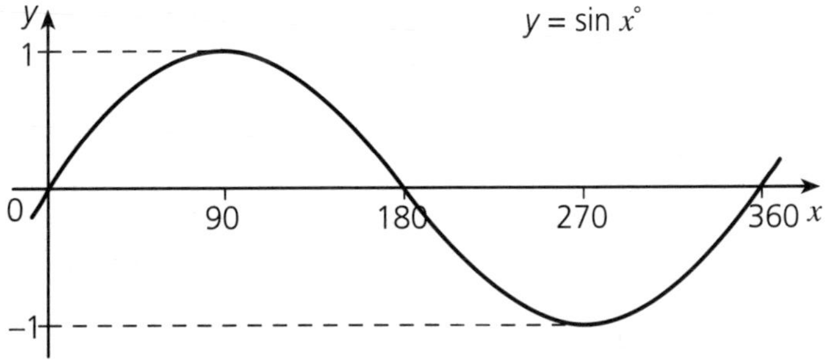

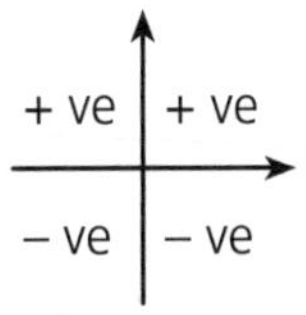

$\sin x^{\circ}$ is positive in the 1st and 2nd quadrants.

sin 0° = 0 sin 90° = 1 sin 180° = 0 sin 270° = –1 sin 360° = 0

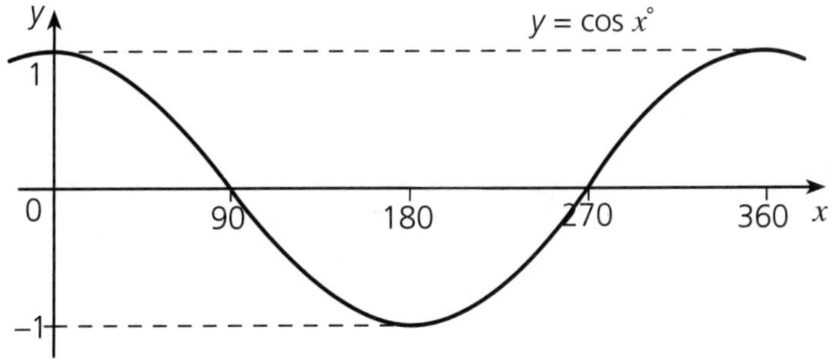

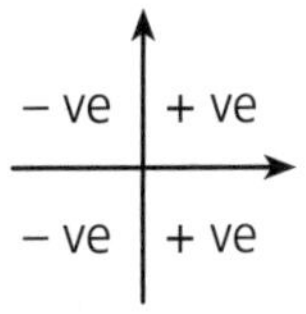

$\cos x^{\circ}$ is positive in the 1st and 4th quadrants.

cos 0° = 1 cos 90° = 0 cos 180° = –1 cos 270° = 0 cos 360° = 1

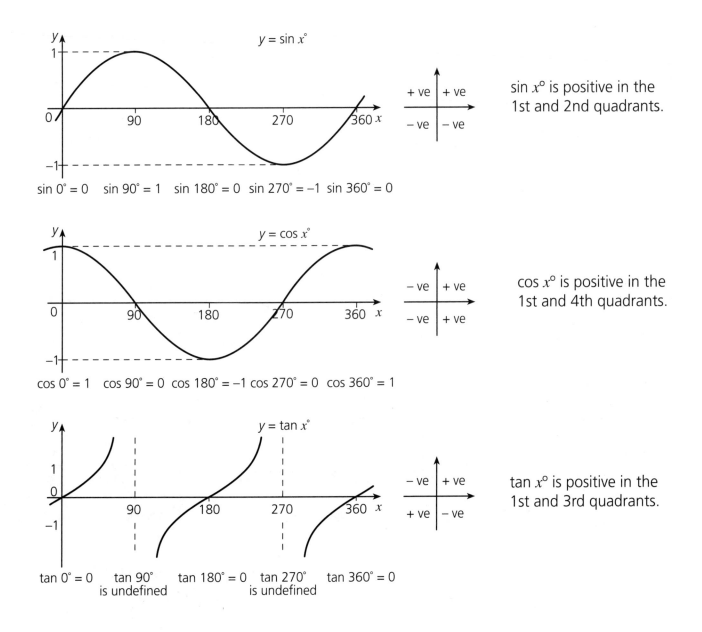

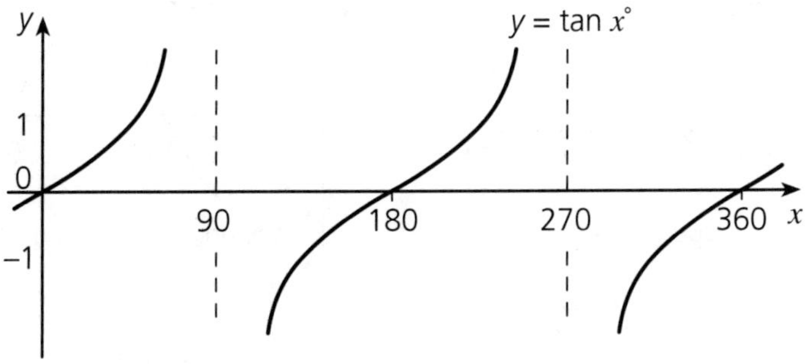

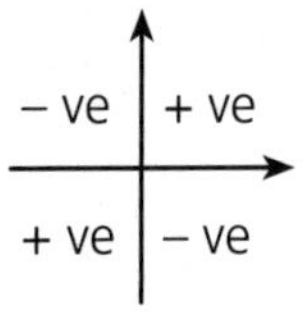

$\tan x^{\circ}$ is positive in the 1st and 3rd quadrants.

tan 0° = 0 tan 90° is undefined tan 180° = 0 tan 270° is undefined tan 360° = 0

12. Further Trigonometry

The summary diagram:

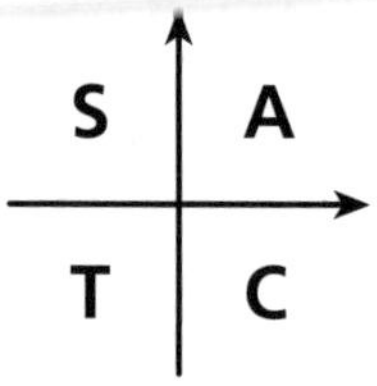

indicates that for angles $x°$ in the
1st quadrant: sin $x°$, cos $x°$, tan $x°$ are **A**ll
positive (**A**) ($0 < x < 90$)
2nd quadrant: only **S**in $x°$ is positive
(**S**) ($90 < x < 180$)
3rd quadrant: only **T**an $x°$ is positive
(**T**) ($180 < x < 270$)
4th quadrant: only **C**os $x°$ is positive
(**C**) ($270 < x < 360$)

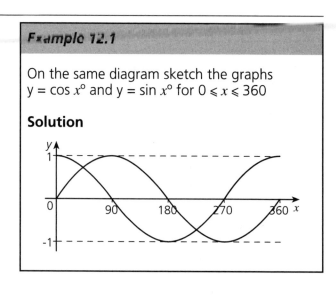

Example 12.1

On the same diagram sketch the graphs
$y = \cos x°$ and $y = \sin x°$ for $0 \leqslant x \leqslant 360$

Solution

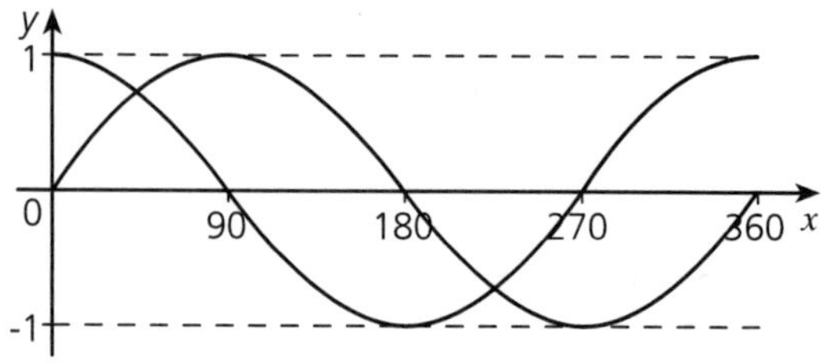

Related Graphs

$y = \sin(x + 60)°$
shifts 60° to the left
amplitude and period unchanged

$y = 2\sin x°$
stretched
amplitude is 2
period unchanged

$y = \sin(x - 60)°$
shifts 60° to the right
amplitude and period unchanged

$y = \frac{1}{2}\sin x°$
squashed
amplitude is $\frac{1}{2}$
period unchanged

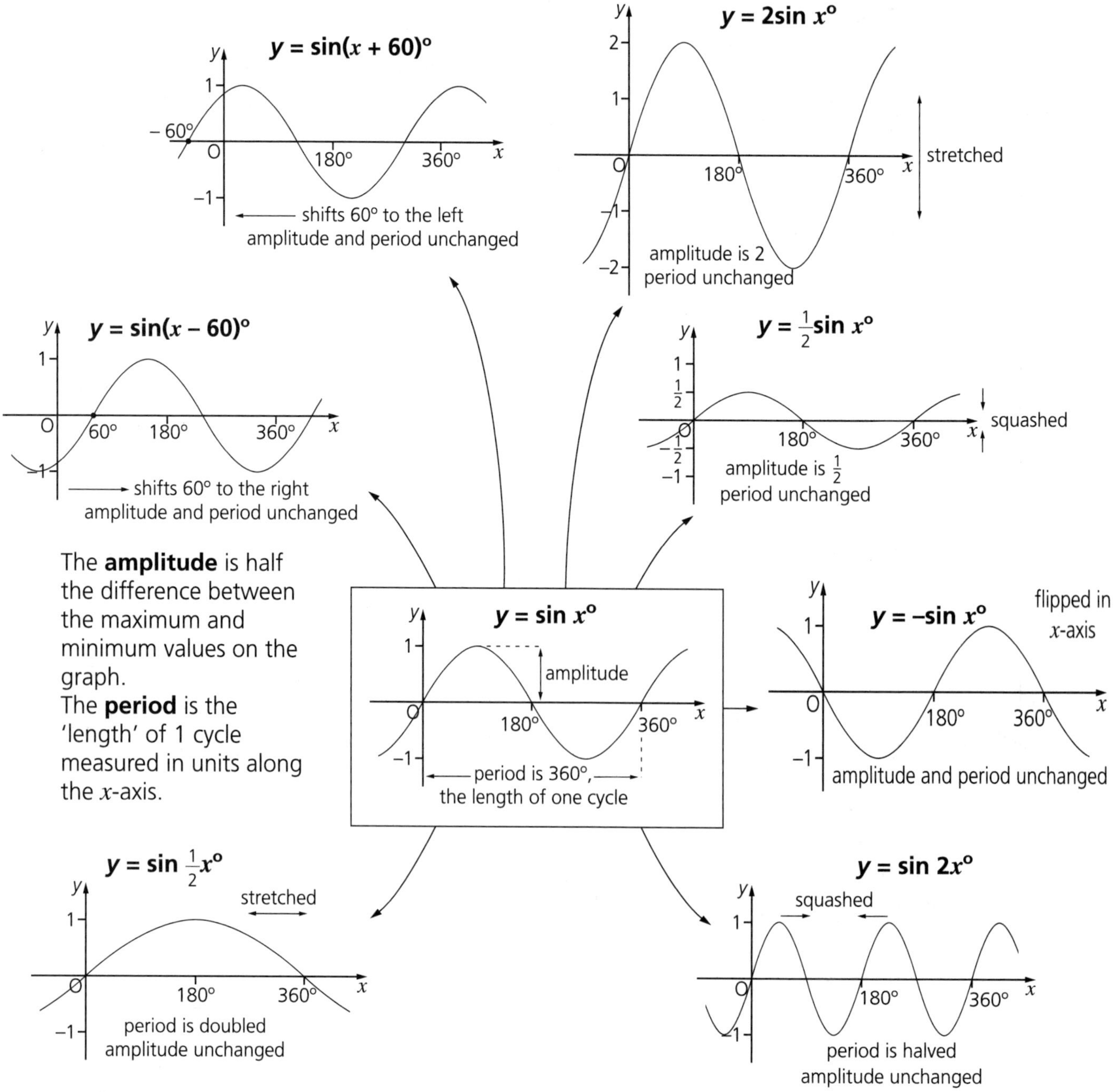

The **amplitude** is half
the difference between
the maximum and
minimum values on the
graph.
The **period** is the
'length' of 1 cycle
measured in units along
the x-axis.

$y = \sin x°$
amplitude
period is 360°,
the length of one cycle

$y = -\sin x°$
flipped in
x-axis
amplitude and period unchanged

$y = \sin \frac{1}{2}x°$
stretched
period is doubled
amplitude unchanged

$y = \sin 2x°$
squashed
period is halved
amplitude unchanged

Here is a summary showing how the graphs of $y = \sin x°$ and $y = \cos x°$ are altered by various changes to the graph formulae:

$$y = k \sin (ax \pm b)°$$
$$y = k \cos (ax \pm b)°$$

- k: For positive values of k the amplitude of the graph becomes k.
- a: The number of cycles will be a instead of one cycle. The period is $\left(\frac{360}{a}\right)°$.
- b: The 'phase angle' b° moves the graph by b° to the left for '+b' or b° to the right for '–b'.

Example 12.2

The diagram shows the graph

$$y = k \sin ax°$$

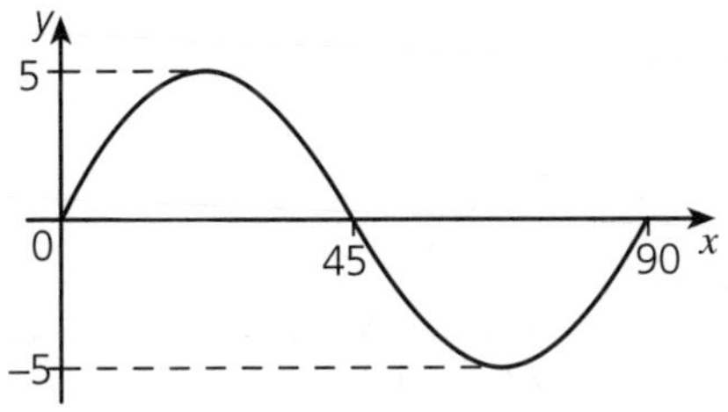

(a) State the values of k and a.
(b) Give the maximum and minimum values of k sin $ax°$.
(c) State the period of the graph.

Solution

(a) The amplitude is 5 so k = 5. From the x-axis scale there will be 4 cycles from 0° to 360° so a = 4.
(b) The maximum is 5 and the minimum is –5.
(c) The period is 90°.

Example 12.3

Sketch the graph

$$y = 2 \cos (x - 45)°$$

for $0 \leqslant x \leqslant 360$, and state the value of x for which $2 \cos (x - 45)°$ has a minimum value.

Solution

The amplitude is 2 and the 'normal' $y = \cos x°$ has been shifted to the right by 45°.

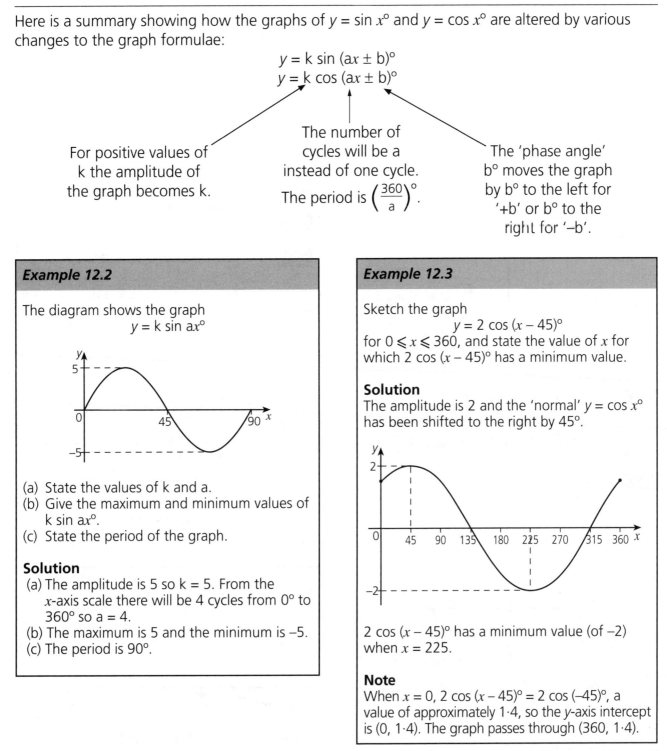

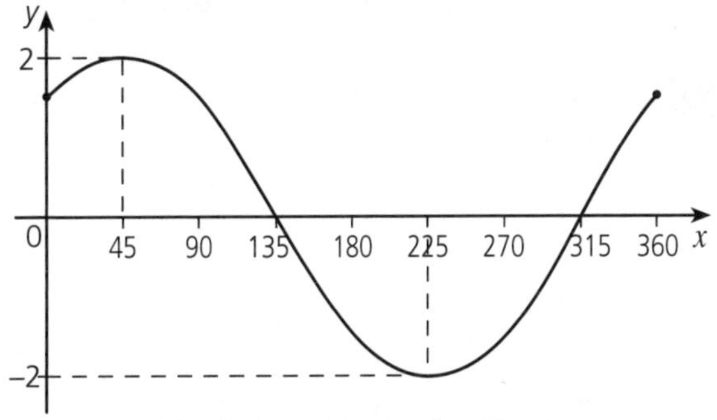

$2 \cos (x - 45)°$ has a minimum value (of –2) when $x = 225$.

Note

When $x = 0$, $2 \cos (x - 45)° = 2 \cos (-45)°$, a value of approximately 1·4, so the y-axis intercept is (0, 1·4). The graph passes through (360, 1·4).

Solving Simple Trig Equations

step 1 Rearrange to get $\begin{matrix}\text{sin, cos}\\ \text{or tan}\end{matrix}$ (angle) = number

step 2 Decide which quadrants the angle is in by using the quadrant diagram:

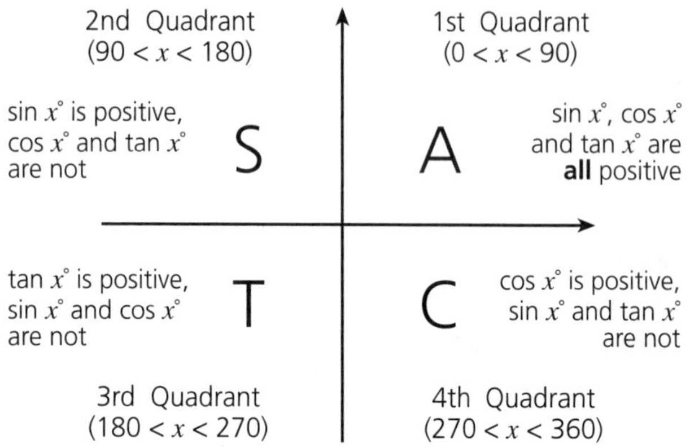

step 3 Find the 1st quadrant angle using the positive value of the number (use sin⁻¹, cos⁻¹ or tan⁻¹ on your calculator as necessary).

step 4 Calculate the required values of the angle using:

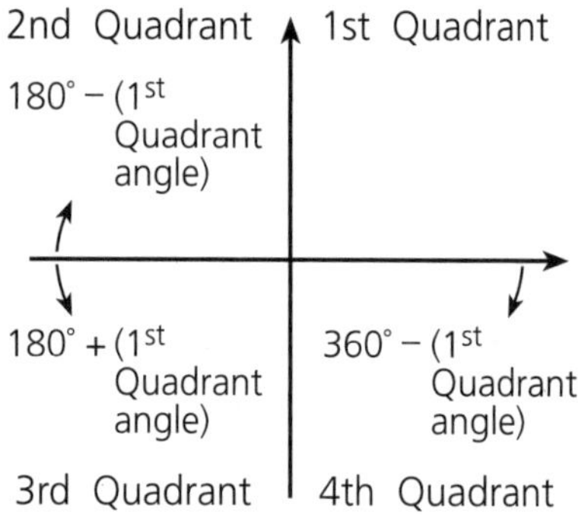

Note

Special equations like:

$\sin x° = 1$, $\sin x° = 0$, $\sin x° = -1$

or $\cos x° = 1$, $\cos x° = 0$, $\cos x° = -1$

are solved by looking at the graph $y = \sin x°$ or $y = \cos x°$.

Example 12.4

Solve $2\sin x° + 1 = 0$, $0 < x < 360$

Solution

step 1 $2\sin x° + 1 = 0$ rearranges to get

$\sin x° = -\frac{1}{2}$

step 2 $\sin x°$ is negative for angles in the 3rd and 4th quadrants.

step 3 The 1st quadrant angle is 30°.

step 4 $x = 180 + 30$ (3rd quadrant) **$x = 210$** or $x = 360 - 30$ (4th quadrant) **$x = 330$**

Note

A graphical check may be made using the $y = \sin x°$ graph:

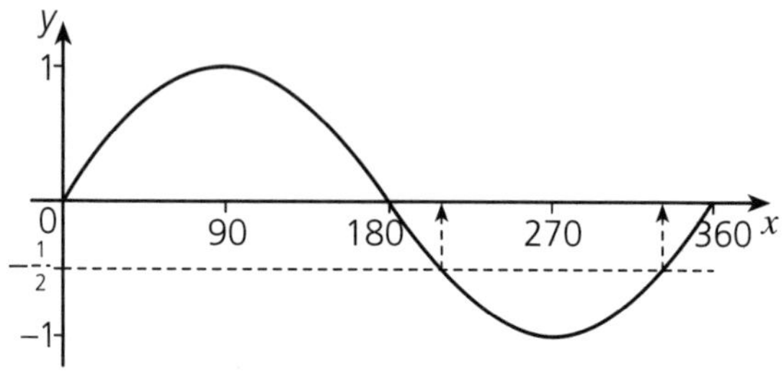

The diagram indicates the two solutions to $\sin x° = -\frac{1}{2}$.

Example 12.5

Solve $\cos x° = 0$ for $0 \leqslant x \leqslant 360$

Solution

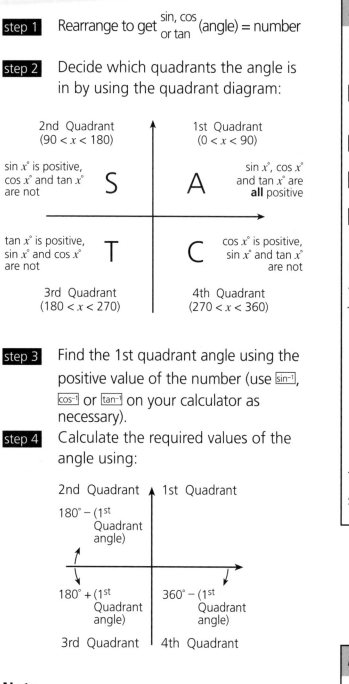

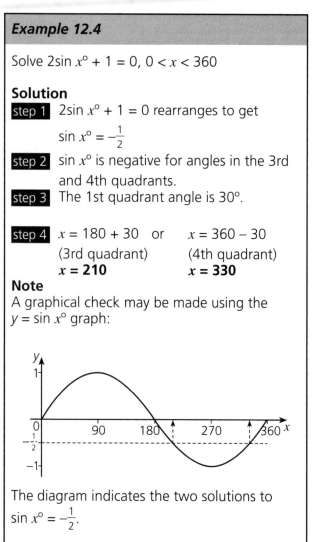

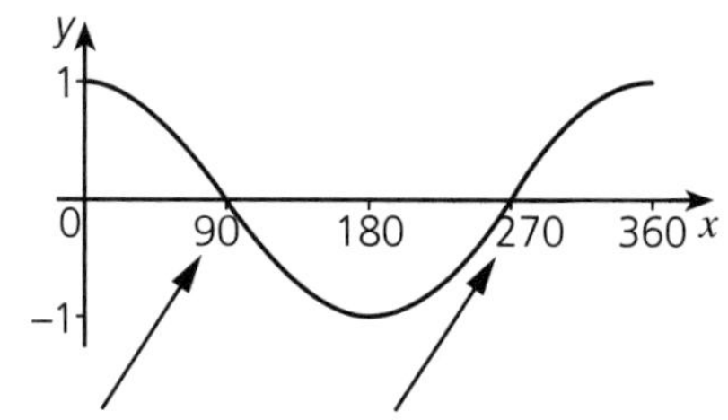

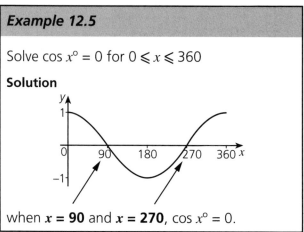

when **$x = 90$** and **$x = 270$**, $\cos x° = 0$.

Some Trig Formulae

Here are two results that are true for all angles x°:

1. $\dfrac{\sin x^\circ}{\cos x^\circ} = \tan x^\circ$

2. $\sin^2 x^\circ + \cos^2 x^\circ = 1$ — rearranging: $\sin^2 x^\circ = 1 - \cos^2 x^\circ$ and $\cos^2 x^\circ = 1 - \sin^2 x^\circ$

Note
$\sin^2 x^\circ$ means $\sin x^\circ \times \sin x^\circ$
$\cos^2 x^\circ$ means $\cos x^\circ \times \cos x^\circ$

Example 12.6

Show that $\dfrac{\sin^2 A}{1 - \sin^2 A} = \tan^2 A$

Solution:

$\dfrac{\sin^2 A}{1 - \sin^2 A}$ — Since $\sin^2 A + \cos^2 A = 1$ then $\cos^2 A = 1 - \sin^2 A$

$= \dfrac{\sin^2 A}{\cos^2 A}$

$= \dfrac{\sin A}{\cos A} \times \dfrac{\sin A}{\cos A} = \tan A \times \tan A$

$= \tan^2 A$ as required.

Index